4ᵈ
Fiil

after
its
kind

"AFTER ITS KIND" DEMONSTRATED IN THE FOSSIL WORLD

Fig. 1. Fossil cockroach from the so-called "Carboniferous" strata, supposed to have lived half a billion years ago. Cockroaches identical with this fossil form are living today. Concerning other species it has been said: "The only difference between a fossil and a recent animal is that one has been dead longer than the other."—Huxley *(Biology and Its Makers,* by Locy, page 335). Fossil from Smithsonian Institute.

after
its
kind

BY BYRON C. NELSON

BETHANY FELLOWSHIP, INC.
MINNEAPOLIS, MINNESOTA

"For the invisible things of Him out of the creation of the world are clearly seen, being understood by the things that are made, even His eternal power and Godhead." Romans 1:20.

Printed in the United States of America
by the Printing Division of
Bethany Fellowship, Inc.
Minneapolis, Minnesota

Dedicated
TO MY WIFE

Foreword

FROM the standpoint of higher education, the twentieth century may well be characterized as **the age of scientism.** Science, in its orginal meaning of "knowledge," has in many areas deteriorated from its God-intended purpose (Genesis 1:28) to the level of an "ism," because it has become a self-contained authoritative world-view that competes with and excludes Christianity. Many scientists today firmly believe that there are no ultimate mysteries in the universe that cannot be fathomed by the human mind through a patient and systematic use of scientific methods and tools. The basis for this belief is the tacit assumption that nothing **has** ever occurred or **can** occur outside the realm of **natural law and processes.** In other words, scientism has no room for the true God.

The theory of organic evolution first arose (and thrives vigorously today) in the atmosphere of this basically atheistic philosophy. Darwin's speculations of a hundred years ago, together with the significant modifications that characterize Neo-Darwinism today, almost completely dominate the intellectual environment of our institutions of higher learning. Not only the life sciences, but also social sciences, the fine arts, and even Western Christianity, have been deeply affected by this all-embracing concept of origins and natural processes. God is no longer honored as the Creator of the earth and living things; miracles are vigorously excluded from the universe as being the crude and childish attempt to explain natural phenomena that characterized a less enlightened, pre-scientific era; and uniformitarian processes in geology as observed today must replace global catastrophes as the mechanism for producing all of the earth's crustal features. Not only is there no personal God for the average evolutionist, but there is apparently no need for one, for man is able to solve his own problems, and is fully able, given enough time in the onward progress of evolution, to bring in his own "kingdom."

The truly amazing thing about this colossal superstructure of philosophic speculation is that it rests upon a foundation of scientific fact that tends to vanish the more carefully it is examined. Here and there, courageous scientists have exposed the non-existence of connecting links between all the basic types of living things, and have insisted that the theory of evolution has no real basis in scientific fact. Others are discovering abundant and impressive evidences in the crust of the earth that catastrophism (rather than uniformitarianism) is the key that unlocks most of the hitherto unsolved enigmas of earth history.

It is obvious, then, that the time has come for a wholehearted proclamation of the creationist world-view as over against the scientifically bankrupt and socially cancerous concept of organic evolution. This proclamation must be accomplished not only by the publication of new books, but also by the promotion of works that have proven their worth through the testing of the years.

Such a work is Byron Nelson's AFTER ITS KIND. First published in 1927, this book has been continually enlarged and revised through sixteen editions, and has achieved unique success as a scientifically dependable, yet popular analysis of the theory of organic evolution. The clear and logical development of arguments, the fine assortment of diagrams and photographs, and the thoroughly Biblical perspective of the book have commended it to many thousands of students, teachers, parents, and pastors in the English-speaking world.

As Byron Nelson's book, AFTER ITS KIND, is reprinted by Bethany Fellowship, Inc., it will be the hope and expectation of many of us that God will use it in a significant way to help stem the tide of unbelief and despair that comes from a refusal to acknowledge the God who created all things and holds the world in His hand.

> John C. Whitcomb, Jr.
> Professor of Old Testament and
> Director of Post-Graduate Studies,
> Grace Theological Seminary
> Winona Lake, Indiana
> September 16, 1967

List of Illustrations

Table of Contents

Chapter I

Clearing the Ground

IN order to help the reader to a satisfactory understanding of the subject of evolution it is necessary to clear the ground of possible misunderstandings by a few definitions and explanations. Among the matters that should be considered are:

WHAT IS MEANT BY EVOLUTION

The word "evolution" has various usages. The growth which is observed when a kernel of corn is thrown into the soil and in due time brings forth a leafy stalk is not what is meant by "evolution," although the term evolution is sometimes used to describe it. The development that has been observed in the modern steamship from Fulton's side-wheeler on the Hudson to the giant trans-Atlantic liner is not what is meant by "evolution," although men speak of the evolution of the steamship, the printing press, the automobile. Nor is "Darwinism" what is meant by "evolution," though the words are sometimes used synonymously. "Evolution," as the word is used in the widespread discussion of the present day, denotes a process which has taken place entirely naturally, without the miraculous intervention of any Divine Being,[1] by which, from out of a single remote ancestor living in the waters of some distant sea, have come all the living things in the

[1] The whole evolutionary *principle* breaks down when any interference from an outside source is admitted. If the supernatural is admitted in one place it cannot logically be excluded in another. If a creative act is admitted once it is thereby admitted in principle that creative acts may have occurred twice or fifty thousand times, and thus that all species may have been created by separate acts of divine volition.

world today. It is a natural process which, if it ever took place, would enable all birds, fish, reptiles, mammals, apes and men to trace their ancestry back from all directions to a speck of protoplasm that somehow came into existence hundreds of millions of years ago. "Evolution" means a process by which man must trace his ancestry back to some ape form, then to some quadruped, thence to some reptile, thence to some amphibian, thence to some fish, thence to an invertebrate, thence to some single celled creature that lived in the slime of the sea. If "evolution" is a fact, then species have never been fixed and are not so now, but have been continually drifting over from one form into another since world history began. This, the commonly accepted meaning of the term, is the one which will be given it in the ensuing discussion.

THE FIRST WORD ON EVOLUTION

A correct understanding of what the Bible teaches regarding the origin of plants and animals is an exceedingly vital matter for those who would have an intelligent understanding of the doctrine of special creation. As will be seen in a later chapter, the most crude misconceptions of special creation prevail among evolutionists and are attributed by them to those who uphold the creation theory.

In chapter one of Genesis we read, "And God said, 'Let the earth put forth grass, the herb yielding seed, and the fruit tree yielding fruit *after its kind,* wherein is the seed thereof upon the earth,' and it was so. And the earth brought forth grass, the herb yielding seed and the fruit tree yielding fruit *after its kind* whose seed was in itself" (Gen. 1:11-12). Concerning the animals that live in the water: whales, fish, oysters, crabs—and those that fly, we read, "And God said, 'Let the waters swarm with swarms of living creatures, and let the birds fly above the earth in the open expanse of heaven.' And God created the great sea-monsters and every living creature that moveth, wherewith the waters swarmed, *after their kind* and every winged bird *after its kind,* and it was so" (Gen. 1:20-21). Concerning the animals that live on land we read, "And God said, 'Let the earth bring forth living creatures *after their kind,* cattle and living things and beasts of earth *after their*

2

kind, the cattle *after their kind,* and everything that creepeth on the ground *after its kind'* " (Gen. 1:24-25).

The Bible is not a text-book of science. In the first chapter of Genesis, however, because it is a matter of the greatest religious importance, the Bible speaks clearly and finally on a matter of biology. *After its kind* is the statement of a biological principle that no human observation has ever known to fail. The most ancient human records engraved on stone or painted on the walls of caves bear witness to the fact that horses have ever been horses, bears have ever been bears, geese have ever been geese, reindeer have ever been reindeer. The most desperate and subtle effort of man in modern times have been unable to alter this divine decree.

The Bible teaches that from the beginning there have been a large number of types of living things, man included, which were so created as to remain true to their particular type throughout all generations. These types or kinds may be fittingly described as *species.*[2] But here a word of

---

[2] Creationists are not all in agreement today concerning what was created according to Genesis. There are those who hold that some other units than *species* were the first forms God made and are the "kinds" referred to in Genesis. They believe the original units were larger—what they call "genera"; or that they were still larger—what they call "families"; or still larger—what they call "orders"; or still larger—what they call "classes"; or still larger— what they call "phyla." But all except *species* are figments of the imagination or arbitrary conceptions. The statement is often made that this is true concerning *species* also, but the statement is incorrect. The *species* have a reality which "genera," "families," "orders," etc., do not have. All biologists, when not contending for the theory of evolution, accept the view of Julian Huxley who said *(Evolution—a Modern Synthesis,* George Allen and Unwin, Ltd., London, 1943, p. 167), "If we ask whether there is any greater biological reality corresponding to the term species than to higher systematic units such as genus, family, or order, we must reply in the affirmative. Thus, Dobzhansky . . . writes . . . 'There is a single systematic category which, in contrast to others, has withstood all changes in nomenclature with amazing tenacity. . . . In most animal and plant groups, except in the so-called difficult ones, the delineation of species is subject to no dispute at all.' And again, 'Despite all difficulty in classifying species in certain exceptional groups of organisms, biologists have continued to feel there is something about species that makes them more definite entities than all other categories.' Bateson has expressed this feeling

caution is necessary. We must determine what a species is. Men often speak as if a *species* is any particular type of plant or animal which possesses marked characteristics of its own and breeds true to form. For example, the fox-terrier is called a species, because it is able to produce off-spring like itself. The dachshund, the collie, the police-dog are called species, because they are able to produce their own particular forms. In this way the human race has been divided into several species according to the shape of the head, the color of the skin, the slant of the eye. But such species are not what the Bible means by the word "kind." The Bible does not mean to say that every distinct form of plant or animal men see about them came from the hand of the Creator in just the form in which it is beheld. It is not the several types of dogs: fox-terrier, dachshund, collie, that were created to remain the same forever, but the one natural species, *dog*. The "kinds" of Genesis refer not to the "systematic" species identified by men, but to those natural species of which the world is full, which have power to vary within themselves in such a way that the members of the species are not all exactly alike, but which, nevertheless, cannot go out of the bounds that the Creator set (Fig. 2.)

In order to make the matter perfectly clear the natural species *man* may be taken as an example. It was *man* that was made, not the Negro, the Chinese, the European. Two human beings whom the Bible knows as Adam and Eve were created, out of whom by natural descent and variation

---

quite precisely, 'Though we cannot strictly define species, they yet have properties which varieties have not, and the distinction is not merely a matter of degree.' Mayr (1940) confirms this from the angle of the taxonomist: 'It is quite amazing that in well-worked groups there is hardly any doubt what is a species and what is not.'" The existence of *species* is so clear and definite that the creationist abandons the only tenable, *genetical* battle-line there is against the theory of evolution, once the *species* have been abandoned, and can then argue only negatively against the theory. No line of demarcation exists, logically or biologically, between genera, families, orders, classes or phyla (and we may as well include sub-kingdoms and kingdoms also), which means that the most extreme theory of evolutionary change must *logically* be admitted, including the theory that men grew out of apes, if the species concept is abandoned.

have come all the varieties of men that are on the face of
the earth. All races of men, regardless of color or size, are
one natural species. They all think alike, feel alike, are
alike in physical structure, readily intermarry, and are
capable of reproducing others of the same character. All
races are descended from two common ancestors who came
full-formed from the hand of the Creator.

The creative acts as they concern the lower forms of life
are shrouded in obscurity. Whether, as in the case of man,
each natural species of the lower animals was started in

Fig. 2. The Biblical concept of a species. Two dogs were created out of which
all the known varieties have come. The decree "after its kind" set the bounds of
their habitation. Within set limits great variation, according to Mendel's Laws, may
occur, and varieties of dogs new and strange to man may be produced. Yet they
are still *dog*. Outside the limits variation cannot go. Not all the varieties of the
dog species are presented here. If these varieties were found in the fossil state
they would be called, in the interest of evolution, distinct species.

a single pair, we do not know. From the analogy of the human species such was very probably the case. A single pair of *dogs* likely was created, from which have come all the 40 or 50 varieties which can be seen in any large dog show, ranging from the tiny Poodle up to the great Dane, with the long line of shapes and sizes in between.

The world contains a species of over forty distinct varieties of cattle, all crossing readily and producing fertile offspring. This cattle species includes such well known domestic beef and milk breeds as the Shorthorn, Hereford, Durham, Angus, Holstein, Jersey, Guernsey, Dexter, Kerry, Devon, Highlander, Park and possibly a number of breeds that are wild. Each of these varieties was not created, but a pair out of which they were all derived. The twenty known varieties of wild and tame hogs of the world in all probability constitute a natural species *pig* that had its origin also in a single created pair.

While the Bible allows that new *varieties* may have arisen since the creative days, it denies that any new *species* have arisen, using the term species to denote natural rather than systematic species. It permits of the view that many new and strange varieties of the kind *pigeon* have arisen through the efforts of pigeon fanciers, but it denies that any of these pigeons is anything but a pigeon or that it may ever produce among its offspring anything that is not a pigeon. The lover of the Bible who would come to a clear understanding of the evolutionary problem and to a firm faith in the Bible doctrine of creation must learn to distinguish between a natural species and the many varieties or sub-species in which God has ordained that natural species may appear.

Only in comparatively few cases do men know exactly what the limits of a natural species are. That there is a limit is the evident teaching of the first chapter of Genesis, but just what forms of life are comprised in certain natural species is not definitely known. It is known pretty accurately what the limits of the *horse* species are : that it does not include the *ass,* since the cross between the horse and the ass is a sterile animal.[3] The limits of the natural species

---

[3] "Sterile" is the term used to denote the fact that a living organism is unable to bear offspring. Its opposite is "fertile."

dog are more definitely known. It includes not only the large variety of domestic animals that we know as dogs, but the jackal, the wolf, and the coyote as well. It does not include the fox, which is another natural species. All forms of *dog* are capable of cross-breeding and producing fertile offspring.

Some forms of life which one would not readily suspect

Fig. 3. A few of the many varieties of the species to which the cabbage belongs— the most widely variable vegetable species known. (1) wild cabbage, (2) kohl-rabi, (3) Brussels sprouts, (4) collards, (5) kale, (6) cauliflower, (7) conical cabbage, (8) Savoy cabbage, (9) broad-leaved cabbage. These varieties are impossible to distinguish in the early stages of growth, and the flowers, seed-pods and seeds are identical. The important thing is that the hundred or so varieties of this natural species cross readily with one another and produce fertile seed, but cross with any other natural species with greatest difficulty. (See *Transactions of the Horticultural Society of London*, Vol. 5, pages 1-43.)

belong to the same natural species are found by breeding experiments actually to be so. (Fig 3.) We quote the prominent student of heredity, Punnett: "It is not visible attributes that constitute the essential difference between one species and another. The essential difference, whatever it may be, is that underlying the phenomenon of sterility. There is little doubt that numbers of well recognized species (i.e., systematic species) will eventually fall to the ground as soon as we are in a position to apply the test of breeding." [4]

Truth derived from observation of nature demands that power of variation be admitted in species. Truth derived from the Scriptures demands that this power of variation in species be limited. Both demands are satisfied by the scientific definition of a species adopted and defended [5] by Prof. William Bateson, President of the British Association for the Advancement of Science 1914-1927: a species is a group of organisms with marked characteristics in common and freely interbreeding. This definition allows for the variation which we know exists in natural species, and yet acknowledges the existence of the wall of partition between natural species known as sterility, which Punnett says is the true test of natural species.[6]

THE VOICE OF THE MULE

From what has been said it is evident that God created plants and animals in such a manner as to enable some species, under certain conditions, to cross with entirely different species and produce what are called "hybrids," a word which originally signified some sort of a monstrosity. This hybridizing takes place more readily among the plants than among the animals. But instead of this

---

[4] *Mendelism,* 6th ed., page 182.

[5] See *Nature,* July 15, 1922.

[6] Darwin tried to blot out the idea that there are such things as natural species and his followers have continued to muddy the truth by saying that what are called natural species are separated from each other by "all degrees of sterility," ignoring the fact that *any* degree of sterility, great or small, is sufficient to keep the species separate, since any degree of sterility will eventually destroy any interspecific hybrid.

8

furnishing evidence against *species* as definite realities and as the original units of creation, it offers most important indications in favor of this very thing—when all the facts are carefully analyzed.

Horses and asses, two definite natural species, which are so much alike that they are classified as belonging to the same genus and are said by evolutionists to have had the same ancestors, possess different numbers of chromosomes in their germ or "marrying" cells. The ass has 32 chromosomes and the horse 19.[7] The products of crosses between horses and asses are "mules," and *male* mules are always completely sterile. No colt has ever been born which has had a male mule for its father. In rare cases, however, *female* mules have produced colts, provided they have been mated with jacks (male asses) or stallions (male horses). But the offspring of these latter matings are such as to show clearly the wide difference between horses and asses.

The situation in regard to female mules which are fertile (and it must be remembered that such animals are extremely rare) is that, insofar as their ability to bear offspring is concerned, they are actually horses. This statement is repeated: Insofar as female mules can be parents at all, they are actually horses. They look like a combination of the horse and ass, but they can only breed like horses. For, whenever a female mule is mated with a male horse (she can never be mated with a male mule because all male mules are sterile) her offspring, if she has one, is in all respects a horse. It looks like a horse and breeds like a horse. And, further, whenever a female mule is mated with a male ass and a colt is born, this colt is in all respects a mule—an animal just like what is produced from an original cross between a horse and an ass. Somehow the female mule loses its power to pass on in its germ-cells any of its ass-parent's nature.

---

[7] While the difference in chromosome numbers is important, it is not as important as it may seem, for other natural species, such as the two similar fruit-flies, *Drosophila Melanogaster* and *Drosophila Simulans* have exactly the same number of chromosomes, yet they have greater difficulty in mating than do the horses and the asses. The characteristics *within* the chromosomes form the vital difference.

Many experiments with the breeding of mules have proved what has been said.[8]

A similar situation to that of the horse and ass exists in the case of the ass and the zebra, a creature belonging to the same genus as the horse and the ass. Like the mule the ass-zebra hybrid is sterile. Still another example is the "cattalo," a type of animal which results from the crossing of bison and domestical cattle.[9] Almost a hundred years ago cattle raisers of the northwestern states began to try to produce a more rugged type of animal for their ranges by crossing bison and cattle, and for the past 35 years the Canadian Government has been working on the same project. No marked success has ever been attained because of the phenomena of sterility which characterizes all crosses between species.

When bison and cattle are mated, nearly all the progeny are born dead, if a bison male is crossed with a cattle female. The mortality is less when a bison female is crossed with a cattle male. But then sterility enters, just as it does in the case of the mule. For, the *male* hybrids of bison-cattle crosses are always sterile. Only *female* hybrids are fertile, and only very few of them. This sterility-of-the-male continues down to the fifth and sixth generation, before signs of fertility in the male hybrids are

---

[8] The above information is from "Fertile Mare Mules," by W. S. Anderson of the University of Kentucky, *Journal of Heredity*, Vol. 50, pages 548-50. Professor Anderson explains the matter of the female mule's progeny's loss of its ass-heredity by saying, "The explanation seems to be, that if the female mule produces an ovum without ass chromosomes, it is viable. It could happen, if in the division of the oocyte, all the ass chromosomes clung together and went into the polar or waste cells, the final ovum would contain only chromosomes received from the horse ancestry. If this hypothetical explanation is true, then the viable ovum of a mare mule would carry the haploid number of horse chromosomes just as the ova of all female horses. On the other hand, no viable ova are produced by female mules except the rare ones, in which the sister polar cells carried away all the ass chromosomes."

[9] Our American domestic cattle readily cross with the zebu of India. Sturdy new strains of range cattle for the warm southern states and Mexico have lately been produced by crossing zebus with our common beef breeds. No trouble at all has been experienced in this because the zebu belongs to the same natural species as cattle and has the same number and type of chromosomes.

noted, and by that time, if not long before, the animals have lost all traces of one or the other of the original parent's nature, not only in outward appearance but in breeding ability as well. A late (1948) report from the Canadian Government says that in its experiments the first fertile male, produced after an original bison-cattle cross, was a domestic bull which had in it 1/32 bison inheritance and 31/32 cattle ancestry. Mossom Boyd, a wealthy cattle-man who performed many years of experiments in crossing bison and cattle said, "An ordinary observer might mistake a three-quarter buffalo for a bison. The one-eighth buffaloes would not be distinguished at all from domestic cattle.[9a]

The results of the crossing of bison and cattle and of many other similar crossings of distinct natural species bear witness to the truth of the statement made by Babcock and Clausen[10] "It has often been observed that the progenies of partially fertile hybrids run back to the parental condition."

Evolutionary biologists claim today that they have produced many "new species" by the crossing of different species of plants, but when their claims are analyzed it is seen that the so-called new species they have produced are essentially the same as mules and cattaloes. Within them is a combination of foreign elements which does not permit them to have the power to survive in changing circumstances which is characteristic of true natural species. They may be called "pseudo-species." Pseudo-species, if they had lasting qualities, which they do not, could never be regarded as causing evolution because they are simply the making of one out of two. Evolution requires the making of two out of one and then some.

For further consideration of natural species the reader is referred to the appendix "Natural Species" in the back of this book.

Within the last half century the study of certain laws of variation and heredity discovered in 1865 and lost and

---

[9a] See *Hybridization of the Domestic Cattle and Bison*—Canadian Government abstract, by Sylvestre, Logan and Muir, 1948. Also M. Boyd, *Journal of Heredity,* Vol. 5, pages 189-198.

[10] *Genetics in Relation to Agriculture,* 1927, page 324.

rediscovered again in 1900 has produced knowledge of facts of tremendous value to those who accept the doctrine of special creations. These laws are known as Mendel's Laws. They will be considered in some detail in a later chapter. Suffice it to say here that the discovery of which we speak gives a clear and remarkably satisfactory view of the manner in which such formations of new varieties out of a common pair as has been suggested could have taken place.

In concluding the discussion of what the Bible teaches it might be said that if the reader would picture to himself a vast number of circles (Fig. 2, 3), and would label each circle with names such as man, dog, cat, pigeon, sheep, and would understand that within each of these circles each species that he has named has varied by interbreeding and produced many forms, yet with never the power to vary so much as to go outside of the circle into the production of a new creature incapable of crossing back again with any of its fellows, and will say "Thus it has been from the beginning," the reader will have a clear, correct, and satisfactory conception of the teaching of the first chapter of Genesis regarding the biological history of animals and plants.

HOW DID LIFE ORIGINATE?

The smallest bit of living matter is the cell. Many different creatures exist which are composed of only a single cell. The bacteria which cause diseases, the yeasts and bread-molds, are of this class. It was believed at the time the evolution theory first gained prominence in modern times that a cell, the simplest living organism, was composed of nothing but slime of some common, liquid material. Then, however, within the cell-matter, by the use of the microscope, was discovered the nucleus, which was found to be a vital part of the life of the cell, controlling the reproduction of its species. Presently the structure of the cell was found to be still more complex, for there was discovered within the nucleus vitally important structures called chromosomes. The end was not yet. Inside of the chromosomes have been discovered what are called the genes, and there is no doubt that higher powered microscopes may reveal still smaller vital structures. The wonder of a cell is apparent when it is realized that out of it comes a frog, or a chick, a guinea-pig with white hair, or a guinea-pig with black hair. No expensive watch can begin to compare with a single cell for complexity of structure. A cell has been described as "a little universe, formed of a host of self-propagating organisms, inconceivably minute and numerous as the stars of heaven." [11] The material of the cell cannot be analyzed. It baffles all attempts to take it apart or put it together, for as soon as such things are attempted the life within it flees and only such dead material as might be swept up off the floor remains.

The coming into existence of one of these bits of life with which the evolutionary process might begin must be explained by evolutionists. When the theory first gained prominence, those who upheld it had no trouble with the problem of the origin of that first living form. When asked how it originated the answer was "by spontaneous generation." Life simply arose out of dead matter spontaneously. When asked if there was any evidence that life could or did originate in this manner, the first evolutionists pointed to the well known fact that in pools of clear water deposited by rain myriads of minute living organisms soon appeared, and also to the fact that in a decaying carcass tiny maggots quickly made their appearance. These were said to be formed spontaneously out of dead matter.

For almost a generation this evidence of how the first living thing originated was considered highly satisfactory to the evolutionists. But in 1846 Pasteur performed those famous experiments that forever destroyed this evidence of spontaneous generation. The way for Pasteur had been paved by a man named Redi, who had the correct idea that the maggots in carcasses were produced by flies laying their eggs in the dead flesh. By screening off the flies he had prevented any maggots from appearing. It was Pasteur, however, who demonstrated that the smaller forms of life, the bacteria, also did not originate by themselves out of dead matter, but came from other bacteria that already existed. By thoroughly sterilizing meat or other food and

[11] Conklin, *Heredity and Environment,* 5th ed., page 210.

13

then preventing any of the bacteria that fly in the air from coming into contact with it, he found that it could be kept for years fresh and wholesome and free from those forms of life that produce decay, whereas other bits of food substances kept in the same conditions but exposed to germs already existing soon became infested with living things. The long accepted "evidence" of spontaneous generation was destroyed by the knowledge that all living things can and do come naturally only from other living things.

With the work of Pasteur the idea of spontaneous generation as an explanation of the origin of life was abandoned as a thing that could be scientifically demonstrated. Other evolutionists, therefore, offered as a solution of the problem the theory that the first bit of life came to this earth from some other planet, carried on a bit of star-dust. This solution met with no approval, for it was obviously only shoving the problem farther away without solving it. The question still remains unanswered by non-believers in creation, and the prospects are that it will ever remain so. "This mystery may, indeed, be forever beyond human understanding." [12]

By all consistent evolutionists the origin of life by spontaneous generation or by transference from some other planet to this earth is held as an act of faith. Not thus to hold it necessitates admitting the supernatural into the evolutionary process. Such an admission, however, consistent evolutionists are totally unwilling to allow, for if it be granted that God made the first cell, it cannot well be denied that He may and could and very likely did create other species by distinct creative acts, as the Bible sets forth. Haeckel said, "The origin of the first monera (living cell) by spontaneous generation appears to us a necessary event in the process of the development of the earth. We admit that this process, as long as it is not directly observed or repeated by experiment, remains pure hypothesis. But I must say again that this hypothesis *is indispensable for the consistent, non-miraculous history of creation.*" [13]

Many evolutionists, like Darwin, are willing to ac-

[12] Vernon Kellogg, *World's Work,* March, 1926.
[13] *History of Creation,* page 348.

knowledge their inconsistency and say that God intervened at the very beginning to bring life into existence. Darwin said, "I imagine that probably all organic beings which ever lived on this earth descended from some primitive form which was first called into life by the Creator."

Still other evolutionists, and these are in the majority, simply and conveniently avoid the question entirely. Without attempting to explain, they assume the first living thing to have come into existence somehow, and then attempt to show how the evolution process went on from that point. They proceed to build in the air, as it were. The reader should clearly realize this weakness in the theory which men would put in place of the Bible doctrine of creation.

SUMMARY

By "evolution" is meant the non-miraculous origin and development of the present world of plants and animals out of a single-celled ancestor.

The Bible teaches that natural species have been the same from the beginning, but that there has been a wide variation within each of them.

The production of new varieties or sub-species within natural species is no justification for the statement that evolution is going on at the present time.

The origin of the first living cell out of which all living things are said to have evolved must, by the evolutionist, be inconsistently attributed to a supernatural act of God, or be assumed, without proof, to have taken place by "spontaneous generation."

CHAPTER II

Their Strong Reasons

THE ground having been cleared somewhat by the foregoing remarks, the reader is invited to proceed to an examination of those "proofs" and "evidences" of evolution that are said to be overwhelming when once they are frankly considered. Each proof will be presented just as fairly as possible. Errors in statements of fact or interpretation will then be pointed out, and the reader left to judge for himself as to whether the proofs offered are as impressive as many have been led to believe.

THE "PROOF" FROM CLASSIFICATION

This proof is taken first, because it is usually so considered in books that are written to advance the theory. The evolutionist looks about the world of living organisms and observes that some organisms are very simple of structure and some are very complex. It occurs to him that it is possible to arrange or classify these organisms in a fairly graded system from the most simple to the most complex, or, as the evolutionist would say, from the "lowest" to the "highest." He therefore proceeds to make an arrangement or classification of all these living things. He begins with the simplest form, some single-celled animal like the *amoeba*. Next to it, or "above" it, he places some simple invertebrate like the *hydra*. Next to or above that he places a "higher" invertebrate like the *star-fish*. Next to or above that he places the simplest form of vertebrate, a chordate like the *amphioxus*. Next to that a fish. Above that an amphibian. Next to that a lower mammal. Above that one of the lower apes. Above that one of the higher apes, and above that *man.* When he is done arranging

16

these creatures, he has a graded system from the simplest living form to the most complex. Then he turns to the creationist and says, "Here is a proof of evolution."

The reader has no doubt already seen the ridiculous absurdity of this mode of reasoning. He has also seen the subtility of it. Absurd as this proof is, because it assumes the thing to be proved, it nevertheless has deceived thousands. We know that old shoes have never evolved. Yet by the above mode of reasoning we could prove that old shoes have evolved, merely by collecting samples of every known kind, and, starting with the smallest and simplest doll's slippers, grade them up in a series through baby's shoes, little brother's shoes, big brother's shoes, mamma's shoes, grandma's shoes, daddy's low shoe's, daddy's high shoes, ending with daddy's high-boots. Taking every kind of shoes known—wooden shoes, sandals, rubber shoes, Chinese shoes, we could grade them all so as to fit them into a tree as the evolutionists do with creatures they wish to prove have evolved, showing how the wooden shoes branched off millions of years ago low down on the stem, how the patent-leather oxfords branched off higher up on the other side, and thus we could prove, without a shadow of a doubt, that no shoe was ever made as it is, but has come into its present state by evolution. We might prove the evolution of the White House by starting with the "lowest" form of house—the grass hut of the savage— placing next in succession all the "higher" houses known, and ending finally with the White House.

The well known biologist and evolutionist, T. H. Morgan, in his book *A Critique of the Theory of Evolution*, admits that the proof from classification is in fact no real proof at all. He says [14] that when the fallacy of the argument is pointed out to pupils of his who believe in evolution they are resentful.

As far, therefore, as the evidence from classification is concerned evolution is not established. It merely begs the question. All creatures, whether simple or complex, may have come into existence at one time, or even the most complex first.

---

[14] Page 9.

THE "PROOF" FROM COMPARATIVE ANATOMY

This second proof is based on the facts that come to light through a study and comparison of the physical structures of unrelated species. It will be presented and considered in three parts.

(1) The proof from comparative anatomy of adult organisms. The student of anatomy studies carefully the skeleton, the muscles, the nerves of one creature, for example, the cat. Then he goes to another species, the dog, for instance, and studies the bones, muscles, nerves, of this species and compares them with the same structures in the cat. From the dog the student goes to the monkey and examines very carefully the structures he finds there and compares them with the same structures in the dog. From the monkey the student proceeds to man and observes carefully the structure of the human skeleton, muscles, nerves, and compares them with what he has already found in the monkey, the dog, and the cat. As he does so it becomes apparent to him that there is a certain similarity of structure underlying them all. The skeletons have all a general similarity in plan. The nerves are alike in design. The muscles are alike.

The student goes to the head of the horse. He finds there certain muscles, some used for twitching the skin of the forehead, some used for moving the ears. He comes back to the head of man. He finds there muscles that correspond to those in a horse. The muscles by which the horse can move his ears well correspond to those by which the man can move his ears poorly. The muscles by which the horse can vigorously twitch the skin of his forehead correspond closely to those by which man slightly moves his scalp. The design or plan of structure of the head muscles of these two unrelated creatures, horse and man, are similar.

Thus the student of comparative anatomy goes the whole round of living things, from those that live in the air to those that live in the sea, and finds the same general plan underlying the structures of vast numbers of them.

Seeing this similarity of pattern or design in so large a number of living things, the student, if he is an evolutionist, says to the creationist, "How can you account for this similarity in so many creatures except on the basis of evolution, except on the basis that one living organism grew out of another, or that all had a common ancestor?" If the creationist is not able to see how it could be otherwise, he becomes an evolutionist, or remains a bewildered creationist. It is the fact of a general similarity in the structures of many animals, together with the suggestion that this similarity is to be accounted for only on the basis of a common evolutionary descent, that constitutes what is said to be one of the strongest arguments for evolution.

Perhaps the reader, if he has never been over this ground, is considerably worried by this "proof." It may seem as overwhelming to him as it has to thousands of misguided young Christians in the colleges and universities where the evolutionary theory is taught. As this sort of evidence is presented in great detail by those who have studied comparative anatomy, and numerous minute likenesses of plan or pattern between creatures pointed out, it often takes greater stubbornness of faith in the Bible, and greater analyzing powers than many young Christians possess, to discern the grave error this line of reasoning contains. The reader is therefore invited to proceed until the mask is pulled off this argument and the fallacy in it revealed.

The criticism of this "proof" does not consist in denying the similarity in plan or structure that comparative anatomy reveals. The likenesses can be admitted in as great detail as the evolutionsists care to have them asserted. *The criticism of the argument from comparative anatomy from the creation point of view consists in admitting the similarity of structure, but in denying the interpretation put upon it, and offering instead another interpretation equally as reasonable and perfectly in harmony with the doctrine of special creation.*

Similarity of plan, pattern, or design may well be a proof of creation. To impress upon himself this fact the reader is asked to call up in his mind a large number of church buildings of various sizes and shapes, none of which are exactly alike, but in all of which there is a general similarity of design. (Fig. 4.) Each may have a tower or steeple. Each may have a large front door. Each may have similar rows of windows. Inside is the same seating

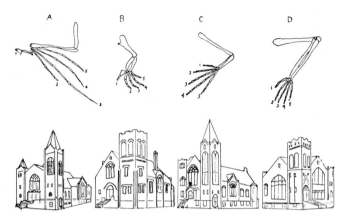

Fig. 4. *Above,* from left to right, are corresponding parts of four widely different species: A. wing of bat, B. forefoot of turtle, C. forefoot of frog, D. arm of man, all built with modifications on the same general plan. This similarity in structure is supposed to prove the evolution of these species from a common ancestral form. *Below* are four churches built with modifications on the same general plan. Since these churches did not evolve, similarity of design can not of itself be said to prove evolution. Similarities in animal structures may be looked upon as evidence of a common plan in the mind of the Creator.

arrangement. Galleries, similar, yet not identical, are found in them all. Seeing this similarity of plan in all these various churches, would any man be so foolish as to contend because of it that the churches evolved from one another or from a common ancestor? Hardly. They were all made separately. They may well have been planned and constructed by one architect at one and the same time. Similarity in design in the case of churches does not prove their evolution. Nor does similarity of design prove evolution in the case of living organisms. The two cases are identical as far as the reasoning in the case is concerned. Similarity in itself proves evolution no more than it proves creation. To the believer in the Bible the similarity of structure in living organisms merely establishes the fact that there was one Great Architect, or Creator, who, when He was about to build many of His species, had in mind one plan or pattern, and this He used for as many creatures as possible with such modifications of the general plan as were necessary for different conditions of existence.

Granting there was a special Creator such as the Bible

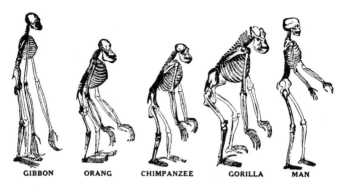

| GIBBON | ORANG | CHIMPANZEE | GORILLA | MAN |

Fig. 5. The "proof" from comparative anatomy in its most subtile and impressive form. The visual impression from such comparisons has a hypnotic influence which leads to a false conclusion that only clear, logical thinking can dispel. What actually is shown by the illustration is that the gibbon, orang, chimpanzee, gorilla and man have somewhat of a similarity in skeletal structure, a fact which there is no reason to deny, since it proves that God created all on a common plan as much as it proves common ancestry. To the illustration could be added in the same position the skeleton of a rabbit, squirrel, sheep, horse and even bird, and the same general similarity would be noted. Until the creationist learns instantly to see the logical fallacy of all such evolutionary illustrations he will be in trouble.

portrays, that Creator might have made His creatures all on a different plan. He might readily have created the dog with four legs, the horse with five, the cow with six, the elephant with ten. He might have shown His ingenuity by making man with three legs and nineteen arms. He might have so constructed sheep that the species might have its nostrils in its back and its ears on its legs. He might have put one kind of nerves or digestive system in man and a totally different system in all of the apes. Is there any reason why He would not do so? Yes. Since all creatures were to live on the same earth under similar conditions, breathing the same kind of air, drinking the same kind of water, eating the same kind of food—it seems reasonable that a Creator would have conceived of one good and excellent plan for all creatures to be constructed upon, the crown of His creation as well as the dumb brutes over which man was to rule, and then modified this plan when modification was wise or necessary. The common plan observable in all creatures may with as good grounds point to one great, economical, and wise Creator as to any evolutionary process.

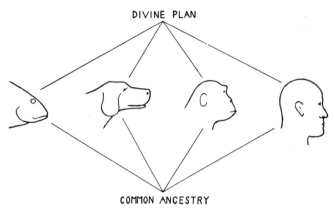

DIVINE PLAN

COMMON ANCESTRY

Fig. 6. One may take his choice. Granting the existence of God, the top explanation of the similarity between "faces" is as reasonable as the bottom.

Consideration of the argument from comparative anatomy might well be left with what has already been said. There remains, however, another angle from which the faultiness of the reasoning underlying it can be seen.

If, as is said, similarity proves that different species have had a common ancestry, then it follows that the greater the similarity between two species, the more closely they are related, and that, conversely, the more unlike two species are, the more distantly they are related. To illustrate, sheep and goats are more closely related than sheep and cats, since there is a greater similarity between sheep and goats than between sheep and cats. But sheep and cats are more closely related than sheep and ostriches, since sheep and cats are more alike than sheep and ostriches. Resemblance as a proof of evolution carries with it the implication that the degree of similarity between species shows the closeness of relationship between them, and is used by evolutionists as a guide in tracing the supposed lines of evolutionary descent, in making evolutionary "trees," in constructing "phylogenies."

But here, in getting away from generalities and down to concrete facts, is where the evolutionary theorist meets his difficulties, for it is utterly impossible very often for him to decide what particular point of similarity in species he

22

shall choose as the basis of their supposed relationships, and the more he studies and becomes familiar with the complexities of living things the more tangled and confused does the situation become for him. God created living things with a common pattern or design in mind, but He varied the pattern so often and so intricately—making forms so much alike in one respect and so different in others, making resemblances between species where the evolutionist would prefer non-resemblances and non-resemblances where he would prefer resemblances—that those who would take the organic world as God has made it and try to fit it into hypothetical trees showing evolutionary lines of descent are continually at a loss what to do. Biologists are continually altering the "genera" and even the "families" to which many species belong, which in other words means that they are changing the species back and forth from one branch of the mythical tree of evolution to another. They are unable to agree among themselves on which branch vast numbers of species belong because these species are similar to species on one branch in one respect and similar to species on another branch in another respect. The great difficulty for the evolutionary tree-makers is that, on the basis of their own argument for evolution from comparative anatomy, species have, as has been said, "too many ancestors."

What we mean will now be shown by a number of definite illustrations. The case of the dolphins, porpoises and whales may first be taken. These aquatic animals are commonly thought to be fish, for in appearance and mode of life they are like fish. On the basis of the argument for evolution based on similarity it is proved, if the argument is valid, that modern fishes and modern whales, dolphins and porpoises are all close relatives, having descended from a common ancestor in very recent times. How else, the evolutionists may ask, can such a similarity as exists between whales and fish be accounted for?

But then, look at the matter from another point of view. Whales, porpoises and dolphins are mammals, like cats, horses, apes. Fishes are cold-blooded creatures, laying eggs. Dolphins, porpoises and whales are warm-blooded animals which develop their young within their own bodies and

23

suckle them on milk. Since there is this inner resemblance among whales, porpoises and dolphins and land animals, whales must have evolved not from fish but from land animals. According to the "proof" of evolution from blood-tests, later to be considered, evolutionists say it is from "the hoofed mammals, especially the swine," that whales have descended. Manifestly, however, this and the other can not both be proved by similarity. The whale can not

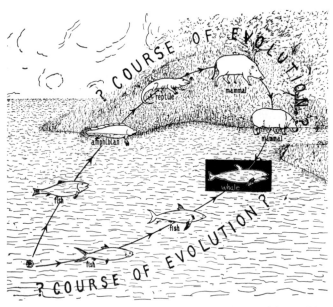

Fig. 7. Too many ancestors. In shape and mode of existence whales are fishes, while in inner structure they are land mammals, like cattle and horses. If similarity of structure is a proof of evolution a contradiction is seen in whales, since they are similar in opposite directions at the same time. Similarity of structure cannot, then, be a proof of evolution.

be descended from a land animal and also from a fish at the same time. Similarity, then, proving a contradiction, is worthless as a proof of evolutionary descent.

We pursue the matter farther. There lives in Tasmania an animal called the "Tasmanian wolf." Its scientific name is "thylacine." In outward appearance it is exactly like a dog. It runs and kills sheep in a dog-like manner. Even from close observation one would say that the thylacine belonged to the dog or wolf tribe of animals. In skeletal structure, head, teeth and so on the thylacine is so dog-like

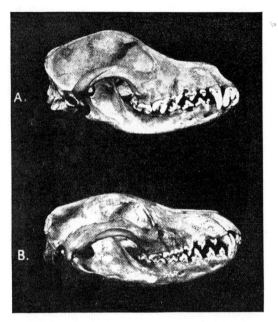

Fig. 8. A. skull of dog. B. skull of thylacine. The skulls (and skeletons generally) of these two species are exceedingly alike. Bone for bone, tooth for tooth they are practically identical. This close similarity proves, according to evolutionary reasoning, that they are very closely related. In other respects these species are totally unlike, since one is a mammal and the other a marsupial, wherefore the evolutionists say they are very distantly related. A contradiction is thus "proved" by comparative anatomy.

that scarcely any difference can be discerned even by the trained anatomist. (Fig. 8.) Surely therefore if, as evolutionists say, anatomical resemblances prove evolution, the wolf, dog, coyote and thylacine are, on the basis of their skeletal similarity, all very closely related to one another by evolutionary descent.

However, the thylacine is totally unlike the dog in matters other than skeleton. There is a large group of animals called the "marsupials." The group includes the kangaroo, opossums, wombats and others. This group is said by the transformists to be very "primitive" in structure and is supposed by them to have evolved directly from the reptiles. The strange feature about the marsupials is that they do not develop their young within the body of the female until they mature, as do dogs and wolves, but bring them forth when they are exceedingly tiny and carry them about in a pouch on the stomach of the female until they are mature. The thylacine is one of the "marsupial" group. It is therefore very closely related by evolutionary descent to the kangaroos, and far, far away from the dogs. This is proved by comparative anatomy, the evolutionists say. But, we ask, how can comparative anatomy prove that the thylacine is very close to the dog and very far away from it at the same time? Something must be wrong with the argument from comparative anatomy.

Still another example is the duck-billed platypus of Australia (Fig. 9). This animal has a bill like a duck and webbed feet. It makes a grass-lined nest and lays eggs which it hatches by curling up on the nest and warming the eggs against its body like a fowl. It must, therefore, have evolved on the same evolutionary stem as the birds. How else can this similarity be explained? But, on the other hand, the platypus has four legs, a fur hide, a tail and claws like many mammals. When it is small it has teeth like a beaver. From these things the platypus must be judged to have evolved with the mammals, not the birds. Again, too many ancestors.

Merely to suggest how numerous are the mixtures of similarities and dissimilarities in the created world of organisms, a few of many more illustrations of this kind may be given. There are two common butterflies in America, one called the Viceroy, and the other called the Monarch. The average person would never distinguish them. They are about of the same size and both have orange and black wings of similar pattern. On the basis of outward appearance the Viceroy and the Monarch butterflies are descended from a close common ancestor, reasoning as do the evolutionists. Their inside structures, however, tell a different story. Inwardly these two species are very unlike and are therefore said by evolutionists not to have descended from a common ancestor at all. Again, there is

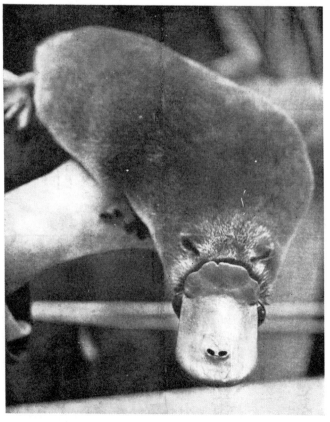

Fig. 9. The duck-billed platypus, a native of the streams of Australia, New Guinea and Tasmania. It has four feet, fur, tail, teeth and claws, but it also has a bill and webbed toes, it makes a nest, lays eggs and hatches them. Hence it must have evolved both from beasts and birds—which is contradictory.

an insect called Criorhina which looks so much like the bumble-bee that bumble-bees receive it as a welcome guest in their nests. Criorhina and bumble-bees must have descended from a close common ancestor if similarity proves evolutionary descent. Inwardly, however, Criorhina is related to the flies and is classified by biologists as a fly and must, therefore, have evolved from that direction. Again, there is an animal called the "Slow Worm" or "Blind Worm" which is indistinguishable outwardly from a worm. Yet inwardly it has the structure of lizards. Evolutionists long called barnacles "mollusks" because of their hard shells, and had them evolving along with clams and oysters, but when it was discovered from an examination of the larvae of barnacles that they were not mollusks but crustaceans (like crabs and lobsters) they transferred the barnacles to the crustacean branch of the evolutionary tree. On the basis of outward form the sea-squirt was also, for many years, regarded as a mollusk, but it was transferred to the vertebrate stem of the evolutionary tree when it was learned that young sea-squirts are tad-poles.

"Convergence" is the name given to the process by which the evolutionists seek to account for the similarities of organisms described above. They say that species have branched away from one another, becoming different, and then have "converged," becoming alike again. This is what makes the whale both like and unlike the fish. About "convergence" we will say nothing except this: if the proof of both evolutionary divergence and evolutionary convergence is comparative anatomy, comparative anatomy must be able to blow both hot and cold in one breath.

(2) The proof from blood-tests. It is in connection with the proof of evolution from comparative anatomy that the much talked of "evidence from blood-tests" should be considered, since it is nothing but the proof from comparative anatomy in another guise.

As a by-product of the scientific investigations which led to the discovery of vaccination there was found about 1900 a test for human blood, a discovery of far-reaching importance in criminal investigations. It is called the "precipitin" test. A liquid called an anti-human serum is made,[15] which, when mixed in certain amounts with human blood in solution, causes a heavy white precipitate to be formed. When this anti-human serum is mixed in the same amounts with the blood of other animals, e.g., the frog, horse, dog, monkey, not so much precipitate is formed. Thus a fairly reliable test for human blood exists.

In 1902 an English evolutionist named Nuttall made use of this precipitin test to find what he called the "blood-relationships" of man to the lower animals. Applying the test—using anti-human serum—to many species, he found that the more nearly like man a species is the more like man's is that species' blood—that is, the greater the amount of the white precipitate does the test produce. In the case of reptiles, for instance, he got no precipitate. In the case of the birds he got only the faintest suggestion of a precipitate. In the case of marsupials (e.g., kangaroos) he got very little. In the case of the carnivora (e.g., dogs, cats) he got more. In the case of the ungulates (e.g., pigs, sheep, horses) he got still more. In the case of the monkeys he got still more. In the case of the apes he got most. Of the apes—the gibbon, orangutan, gorilla, and chimpanzee—the last two gave the greatest amounts of precipitate. And these results, this proof that there are various degrees of similarity between human and other bloods—the least similarity in bloods being between that of men and that of reptiles (between whom also there is the least similarity in general physical appearance) and the greatest similarity in bloods being between that of men and that of apes (between whom also there is the greatest likeness in general physical appearance)—is said to prove the theory of evolution.

We have stated the case in the most favorable way possible for the cause of the evolutionists. But who can not see that we have here, only in a different garb, the same false reasoning we have been considering, namely, the erroneous argument that similarity proves evolution? Simi-

---

[15] It is made as follows: The clear, colorless serum of human blood is injected in increasing amounts into some animal like the rabbit. After a large amount has been injected and the animal has become used to it, the animal is killed. Its colorless blood serum is then drawn off and is the anti-human serum used in the tests.

larity does not prove evolution any more than it proves creation, whether that similarity is found in structure of skeleton, muscles, nerves, blood or anything else. Similarities existing between different organisms may be said to show that there was one Great Architect who, when He made the organic world, used a common plan. In this case the common plan is seen in the structure of the blood.

If close similarity in blood structure proves the evolution of certain animals from one another, what must the evolutionists conclude from the established fact that the chemical substance called thyroidin—the active principle of the thyroid gland—has precisely the same composition in sheep as in man and as far as we know in all other animals with a thyroid? If similarity proves evolution, what does identity argue? What is argued by the fact that the milk of asses is more like that of human beings than is the milk of any other animal? What is argued by the fact that when a man is sick with "Haemophilia," a disease which causes profuse bleeding even from slight wounds, and the blood-serum of a rabbit is injected into him, very favorable and curative results follow, whereas, if the blood-serum of an ox is injected it acts as a poison and dangerous symptoms result? What is argued from the fact that Malta fever affects, so far as we know, only man and goats, while plague occurs only in man and rats? [16]

Facts such as the above display a side of the matter which evolutionists do not emphasize. Nevertheless such facts do not offer the best answer to the evolutionary argument based on blood-tests. It can and should be admitted by the creationist with perfect readiness that blood-tests such as Nuttall carried out point to the same general sort of similarity between God's creatures as do other tests of comparative anatomy. The ape is certainly, when we consider its bones, muscles, nerves and so on, more like man than is a turtle or a fish, and we would be much surprised if Nuttall did not find that the blood of an ape and that of a man showed greater similarity also than did the blood of a fish or turtle and that of a man. The horse, when we consider the structure of its bones, muscles, nerves and so

---

[16] See Zinsser, *Infection and Resistance*, pages 52-55.

on, is more like a man than is a fish or turtle, though less like a man than is an ape, and it would be odd indeed if blood-tests did not reveal that the blood of a horse is more like that of a man than are the bloods of snakes and turtles, although less like man's than is the blood of an ape. Sheep and deer are certainly more alike than are sheep and tigers, and it is not strange at all that the bloods of sheep and deer are more similar than are the bloods of sheep and tigers. Such things have been shown by blood-tests. But these things, we maintain, do not prove evolution any more than they prove that God created all these creatures on a common plan with modifications.

(3) The proof from comparative embryology. It is in association with the proof from comparative anatomy that one phase of the so-called proof from embryology ought also to be considered.

Just as the student of comparative anatomy has made a comparison of the structure: skeleton, muscles, nerves, of many adult forms of life, and found them to reveal a common plan, so the student of comparative embryology has made a comparison of the modes of development of the various embryos and found there also a common plan.

Each individual organism, whether very simple or very complex, begins its existence as a single cell. That one cell divides to form two cells. Each of these two cells divides to form four cells. These again divide to form eight, then sixteen, then thirty-two and so on up until the adult form is complete. All species, from man down to the simplest invertebrates, thus begin as single cells smaller than the head of a pin and similarly increase by division and growth and redivision and growth. As the masses of tiny embryonic cells grow in size, the embryos of all species form what is called a "blastula," which, though it is not necessary to describe it, may be said to be roughly similar in all embryos. Some very simple creatures which live in ponds (e.g., volvox) practically cease development with the blastula stage and after some further modification live as adults in a form which looks like a blastula. The "blastula" stage is followed in the course of growth by a formation called the "gastrula," which is also a parallel stage in most embryonic developments. The gastrula is

31

the beginning of the stomach. Some form of life (e.g., jelly-fish) cease development at the gastrula stage. Here they turn off and are developed for adult existence in water as gastrula-like animals. (See Fig. 10.) After the gastrula

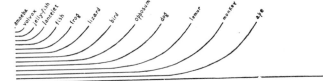

Fig. 10. Diagram illustrating the similarity or parallelism in the embryonic development of the lower animals and man. From the germ-cell up through the various stages to the adult the embryos travel parallel tracks. After developing in a manner similar to the development of the human being, the embryos of the lower animal forms turn off and mature as God decreed they should. This similarity of development, like the similarity in adult structure, points to a common design in the mind of the Creator. The various paths of development are not identical or exactly parallel. Each species shows characteristic differences, and the parallelism is often hard to discern.

stage has been passed a faint streak appears, called the "primitive streak." It marks the beginning of the spinal column. One creature, the lancelet, turns off here and becomes modified for adult life in this form. As development continues a very simply constructed heart and certain arteries are added.[17] Here the fish turns off the common road and becomes modified into a true fish. The arteries become modified into the gills of the adult fish. As development continues a simply constructed kidney is added, and the heart and arteries are made a little more complex in structure.

About here the frog turns off from the common course. Thus, step by step, new structures are added, which

---

[17] The simple heart and the arteries (called "aortic arches"), which in the embryonic development of the fish become modified into gills after the turn-off from the common path, are also present in a somewhat similar form in the human embryo. These facts form the basis of the statement made by evolutionists that each man is at one stage in his life a "gilled-creature." This matter will be discussed more fully in the section on embryology, but here it may be said that no structures in the human embryo are gills or ever become gills. Even in the fish embryo the arteries are not gills. They are structures which, only after much modification and further development, *become* gills.

32

roughly resemble one another in all vertebrate embryos, and the old structures are made more intricate and complicated, until finally all structures are present and developed into their most perfect and ideal form in man.

That there is this similarity in the development of creatures is undeniable. Since each species develops in its own peculiar way the similarity is often much concealed, yet it is there. This similarity in development is pointed to by the evolutionist as a "proof" of evolution, for how else, he asks, can it be accounted for. The answer is simple. As the similarity between *adult forms* can be accounted for on the basis of a common plan in the mind of the Creator, so the similarity in the *development* of the adult forms can also be accounted for. Both, showing a common plan, furnish arguments for special creation.

THE "PROOF" FROM EMBRYOLOGY

This proof consists essentially in the so-called fact that each embryo in its development from a single cell to adult form passes through stages that correspond one after another to each upward step in the evolution of the species as a whole. According to the theory man has evolved from a single cell in some primitive ocean into an invertebrate, thence into a fish, thence into an amphibian, thence to a reptile, thence to a mammal, thence to an ape, finally becoming himself, with thousands of nameless transition stages in between. Therefore, so it is said, the embryo of man begins as a single cell, passes into a fish, thence into a reptile, thence into a mammal, thence into an ape, and finally ends in man.[18] In other words, the embryological development of man is a moving picture of 500,000,000 years of human history.[19]

The above is the argument for evolution from embryology in its boldest form, as it was formulated by Ernest

---

[18] Childhood is further said to represent the stage of the development of the race through the low savage-stage. Children like to throw stones and chase one another with sticks!

[19] In the language of the evolutionists "Ontogeny (i. e. the history of the individual) is the recapitulation (repetition) of phylogeny (i. e. the history of the race)"!

Haeckel the latter part of the last century.[20] That the embryo passes through such stages is a wild statement not supported by the facts. Each embryo must develop somehow in order to reach the adult condition, and, as has been shown in the preceding section, there is a vague similarity in the development of all embryos. But it is only a prejudiced imagination that is able to see in the embryonic development a retracing of any such evolutionary history as the theory of evolution supposes. The evolutionist, Locy, says, "Many stages have been dropped out, others are unduly prolonged or abbreviated, or appear out of their

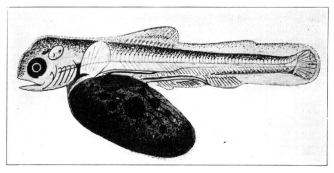

Fig. 11. A stage in the embryonic development of the fish. According to the old argument for evolution from embryology each creature in its development from a single cell to adult form repeats each stage through which its ancestors evolved. Above is one stage in the embryonic development of the fish that must be called a "falsification of the ancestral record." for no creature like the above ever could have existed.

chronological order. And besides, some of the structures have arisen from adaptation and are not, therefore, ancestral at all, but are, as it were, recent additions to the text. *The interpretation becomes a difficult task,* and requires much balance of judgment and profound analysis." [21] None but an evolutionist, we suppose, is privileged to have the necessary "balance of judgment."

[20] Today no evolutionist of any standing dares to repeat it in the form which Haeckel presented it. "Haeckel saw in it (the evidence of embryology) more than the actual facts warranted and by his over-emphasis of its significance and his detailed interpretation of the evolutionary history brought it into some disrepute." Kellogg, *Evolution the Way of Man,* page 54.
[21] *Biology and Its Makers,* page 230.

The following facts regarding the proof from embryology deserve special attention:

(1) It is admitted by evolutionists that there are embryonic stages which do not resemble any possible ancestral forms. Morgan, in his *Critique of the Theory of Evolution,* provides pictures of several embryonic forms which, he says, "could not possibly represent ancestral animals." [22] He shows the picture of an embryonic fish (See Fig. 11) which has attached to its stomach region a sac as large as itself, and another picture of an embryo chick which at an early stage is so completely enveloped in a membrane that had it ever existed in such form, it would have been shut off entirely from the outside world. An example of a stage that can not possibly resemble any ancestral animal may be taken from the insects, e.g., the common house-fly. Let an evolutionist describe the embryonic life of this fly. "A maggot hatching from an egg grows so rapidly that it is mature in a few days; then within an impenetrable skin (i.e., the chrysalis) it dissolves itself almost completely. A little later the liquid content of the skin turns to a sort of jelly, and in a few days this is reconstructed into a being so totally different in appearance, in habits, and in structure, that the resources of science find themselves severely taxed to demonstrate any identity in the organs of the two stages of the insect's existence." [23] Special attention is called to what is said about the maggot's *dissolving* itself into a *liquid*. The maggot, according to the evolutionists, represents an ancestral animal. The dissolved stage following does not. Why not, we ask. Why say one does and the other does not?

"During the period of life within its womb the human embryo develops a large organ like a sucker, which is closely pressed against the wall of the womb and which enables the tiny baby to suck nourishment from its mother's blood. This sucker, which is called the placenta, is developed from the belly of the embryo, which is thereby distorted out of shape." This description is quoted from

[22] In evolutionary terminology embryonic stages which represent ancestral animals are called "palingenetic." Those that do not are called "cenogenetic."

[23] W. F. Showalter in *National Geographic,* July, 1929, page 66.

the evolutionist McBride, who also says, "Now no one imagines that some ancestor of man went about through life with a placenta protruding from its under surface." [24] But we ask, why not, if embryological development shows past history? We grant that no human ancestor did go through life thus, but if the reasoning underlying the embryological proof of evolution is valid he did. It is during the same time the human embryo has a placenta protruding

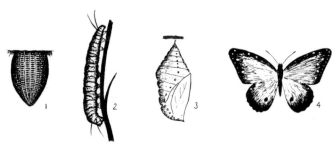

Fig. 12. Four stages in the embryonic development of the Milkweed Butterfly. (1) egg, greatly enlarged. (2) larva. (3) pupa or chrysalis. (4) young butterfly, reduced. The larval or worm stage is said to repeat an ancestral animal. The chrysalis stage, in which many species of butterflies spend half their lives, is said not to repeat an ancestral animal. The chrysalis stage is a "falsification of the ancestral record," since it is a stage in which the butterfly spends a long, quiet, helpless existence without taking in food. Two questions may be asked: First, why is the larval stage ancestral and not the chrysalis? Second, why and how did the worm, through thousands of years, evolve itself into such a helpless form as the chrysalis, and how did it manage to evolve out of it?

from its stomach that the embryo has certain structures that are supposed to prove that man recapitulates a fish. But why regard this last as a record of the past history of man and not the first? If evidence is to be valid it must all be taken. If man can choose what he likes from evidence and reject what he does not, he can establish any falsehood.

Morgan says that "hundreds of such embryonic cases are known to embryologists and are explained as "falsifications of the ancestral record." [25] The absurdity of this proof from embryology is apparent when those who advance it must accuse nature of falsifying. It would seem more proper, if, when natural evidence gives the lie to a theory,

[24] *Creation of Evolution*, 1928, page 56.
[25] *Critique of the Theory of Evolution*, page 17.

the theory and not the evidence should be considered to be "falsifying."

(2) It is admitted by evolutionists that the vast majority of embryonic stages which are supposed to resemble remote ancestors are absent entirely. Only three definite ancestral evolutionary stages are said to be revealed. They are:

(a) The "fish" stage. It is said that the embryos of man, cats, dogs, and birds all have gills and gill-slits at an early stage of development, these gill-slits being relics of the days when man was a fish. Here the imagination of the evolutionist is active, or else his regard for accurate statement is lax. To say that the early embryonic folds, clefts, and arteries which appear as somewhat similar formations in all vertebrate embryos, whether of man, ape, bird or fish, are gills and gill-slits is not warranted by facts. This can not be too emphatically stated. These things can not properly be called gills *even in the fish embryo.* In the case of the fish embryo they are structures that *become* gills, a far different matter from already being gills. In the case of the human embryo and those of dogs, cats and so on they become ears, jaws and parts of the head and neck. It is just as reasonable to say that the embryonic structures in the fish embryo are human ears, jaws and neck as to say that the somewhat similar structures in the human embryo are gills. What would be thought of the man who, seeing three similar piles of brick in a brickyard, the first pile to be made into a house; the second pile into a store; the third pile into a church, should say of the pile of brick to be made into a house, "That is a house"; and of the pile of brick to be made into a store, "That is a house"; and of the pile of brick to become a church, "That is also a house"? That is like what the evolutionists do when they say of the embryonic structure of land animals, "These are gills." That man is never a "gilled-creature," as is so often said by evolutionists, is clear from the fact that the creases between the early folds of the human embryo never open. In the fish embryo they become open only by the time the embryonic development of the fish is fairly complete. "In gill-bearing animals the grooves become complete clefts, the 'gill-clefts,' opening from the pharynx on to the interior; perforation, however, does not occur in birds and mammals."[26] "In all air-breathing vertebrates true gills are lacking,"[27] admits Prof. Conklin.

(b) The "tail" stage. Usually books on evolution do not mention any tailed ancestor as being represented in any human embryonic form. However, when a book on evolution is intended for the general public some evolutionists dare to make the statement that the human embryo has a tail. Kellogg, in his latest book[28] says, "The tail is longer than the leg in early stages of the human embryo, but gradually becomes more and more reduced, until at birth there is no external sign of it."

Here again fancy and facts do not agree. The adult human being has thirty-three vertebrae in his spine. The spine of the human embryo also has thirty-three vertebrae and at no time more, which would be the case if the embryo ever in actual fact had a tail. That which is called a "tail" is nothing but the extension of the embryonic spine.

Some conception of the vagueness of the evidence involved in this proof of evolution, and of the room for the imagination to work, is had when it is realized that at this early stage of embryonic development, when man is said to be a "tailed" and a "gilled" creature, the embryo is the size of a pea. At that time only the principal organs of the body are in existence and these only in their faintest beginnings. They are, furthermore, not in their proper place. The heart is at this time as large as the head and is located in front of the mouth region. The spinal column is well marked long before there are any indications whatever of legs or arms.

The absurdity of seeing in the extension of the spine beyond the legs a true tail is most apparent when it is known that the intestine also extends beyond the legs, along with the so-called tail, and is, as Kellogg says of the tail, also "longer than the leg in early stages." Near the end of the so-called "tail" is the anal opening.

---

[26] Gray's *Anatomy,* 15th edition, page 1168.
[27] *Creation by Evolution,* page 67.
[28] *Evolution the Way of Man,* page 52.

(c) The "hair" stage. The following statement appears in Prof. Kellogg's book:[29] "At the seventh month of prenatal life the chimpanzee and gorilla have well developed hair on scalp, eyebrows, and lips and the rest of the body is covered with fine hair. This is also true of the human embryo of the same age and the hair slopes and lines are very similar to those of apes. But before birth the human embryo loses the fine body hair." Such statements as these have influence only because of the ignorance of the ordinary person regarding the actual facts.

In considering the weight of this argument one can do no better than note what is said in several standard embryology books, and draw his own conclusions. The implication of the above statement is that the fine hair with which the embryo ape is covered at seven months and the fine hair with which the human embryo is covered are exactly alike. Nothing could be farther from the truth. The hair of the human embryo is exceedingly fine compared with that of the embryo ape. Heisler [30] says of the human embryo, "The first growth of hair is unpigmented and is extremely fine and soft and is known as the lanugo or embryonal down. This appears upon the scalp and some other parts of the body in the fourth month, gradually extending over the entire surface in the succeeding months. In the eighth month the lanugo begins to disappear, but is not lost as a whole till after birth when the permanent growth of hairs takes its place. Upon the face, in fact, the lanugo persists throughout life." Minot [31] says, "Lanugo is the term applied to the first coat of hairs in the embryo. . . . The hairs are fine compared with those of the adult and are therefore usually described as woolly hairs. They are lost from most parts of the body and are replaced by larger and coarser hairs. Over the face the lanugo persists throughout life, but owing to the fineness and loss of color is not noticed." The attention of the reader is called to the emphasis placed on the fineness of the hairs. So fine are they in fact that if the

---

[29] Ibid., page 61.

[30] *Textbook of Embryology*, page 250.

[31] *Human Embryology*, page 561.

39

reader ever has the opportunity to visit medical museums and study the exhibitions of human embryos from five weeks to the age of birth he will not with his naked eye be able to see the faintest sign of a hair except on the head and eyebrows. Bailey and Miller [32] say, "The fine-formed hairs, which are exceedingly fine and silky, develop in vast numbers over the surface of the embryonic body and are known collectively as the lanugo. This growth is lost beginning before birth and continuing during the first and second years except over the face, and is replaced by coarser hairs. These are constantly shed during the life of the individual and replaced by newer ones. The new hairs probably in most cases develop from the old follicles."

If the reader is interested in knowing just what the hairs are like that appear in the fourth month and are on the body when it is born and remain only on the face during life, for the clothes wear them off elsewhere, he can take a mirror and step to the window and, looking carefully, see them along the outer edge of his ears.

The actual value for the theory of evolution of the evidence from embryology, when all the facts are clearly understood, was expressed by Bateson before the assembled scientists of America when he said regarding this argument, "Today we feel silence to be the safer course." [33] Other evolutionists have expressed the same sentiments in complete form but in more technical language. E. B. Wilson, called the "dean of American embryologists," has had this to say, "It is no wonder that a strong reaction against the theory has set in—that faith in the embryological record is giving way to skepticism and indifference. There is a strong suspicion that the embryological record has somehow failed, and there are even some morphologists who seem almost ready to abandon the entire recapitulation theory." Wilson quotes with approval Gegenbaur, who said, "But if we are compelled to admit that cenogenetic characters (i. e. those supposed *not* to represent ancestral stages) are intermingled with palingenetic

[32] *Textbook of Embryology,* pages 447-448.
[33] *Science,* Jan. 20, 1922.

40

(i. e. those that *are* supposed to represent ancestral stages) then we can not regard ontogeny (i. e. embryonic development) as a pure source of evidence regarding phyletic relationships (i. e. evolutionary history). Ontogeny, accordingly, becomes a field in which an active imagination may have full scope for its dangerous play, but in which positive results are by no means everywhere to be attained. To attain such results the palingenetic and the cenogenetic phenomena must be sifted apart, an operation which requires more than one critical *granum salis*. If it is once admitted that not everything in development is palingenetic, and that not every ontogenetic fact can be accepted, so to speak, at its face value, it follows that nothing in ontogeny is immediately available for the critique of embryological development. This conclusion can not be escaped." [34]

Referring to the above words of Gegenbaur, Prof. Conklin has said, "Since the time this was written there have been many less moderate utterances to the same effect, some even declaring that there is no evidence that ontogeny ever recapitulates phylogeny and that Haeckel's 'biogenetic law' has no foundation in fact." [35] One of the "less moderate utterances" Conklin probably referred to is that of Montgomery, a biologist of high standing in evolutionary circles, "The recapitulation hypothesis is scientifically untenable." [36]

THE "PROOF" FROM VESTIGIAL ORGANS

This fourth proof of evolution rests on the so-called fact that there are in the bodies of many animals parts that have absolutely no function. These parts, it is said, lost whatever usefulness they once had in the course of evolution. As an illustration of what a vestigial organ is, we might take the old kerosene lamps that were once beside the windshield of the early automobile. Now those kerosene lights are no more. Strong electric head-lights have taken their place. If, however, the old kerosene lamps

---

[34] *Biological Lectures—Woodshole,* 1894, page 104.
[35] *Creation by Evolution,* 1928, page 71.
[36] *The Analysis of the Racial Descent in Animals,* 1906.

were still retained in manufacture because they could not be gotten rid of, they would be what would be designated as "vestigial" organs of the automobile. Such vestigial parts are supposed to be present in great abundance in the bodies of animals and men, especially the latter, and are being carried around as so much useless luggage.

It is certainly not reasonable that the Creator would put into any one of His creatures parts that are of absolutely no use to it. Certainly He would not put in detrimental parts. The only way of determining the value of this argument, therefore, is to determine whether there are in any creature parts that serve no purpose. It makes no difference what degree of functional importance the parts may have. It is not to be expected that all parts of a body should have equally important functions. The thumb could better be dispensed with than the heart. If a part serves any function whatever, whether it is only in the embryonic period, in the years of childhood growth, or later, that part is useful and cannot reasonably be considered a proof of evolution.

Certain definite organs of men and animals that are said to be "vestigial" will now be considered. So many have been enumerated that it is impossible in these pages to mention them all. Furthermore, it is not necessary. The chief ones will be considered and certain principles will be stated that will serve the purpose of showing the fallacy in this sort of proof.

It should be borne in mind, as was brought out in the section on comparative anatomy, that the Creator has used one common plan or pattern of structure for vast numbers of His creatures. However, since these creatures were to live in different surroundings, it was necessary that the common plan should be modified, now in one place, now in another. Man is one of the creatures made on the common plan. In his body he is not essentially different from the lower animals. According to the Bible it is in his spiritual nature that man is superior to, and a creature totally different from, the dumb brutes.

It is to be expected, in view of the similarity of plan of structure which the Creator adopted, that we should find

42

in the body of man the same muscles and organs which we find in the lower animals, only modified according to human needs. Such is the case. In the head of the horse, for example, and this matter is referred to because it touches the subject of vestigial organs, are certain muscles that are very useful to the horse, muscles by which the horse can twitch the skin of his forehead vigorously to drive off flies, and muscles by which he can turn his ears back and forth quickly in order to detect danger. In man, because he is made on the same fundamental plan as the horse, these same muscles are found, only they are not so highly developed and efficient. With them man can move his ears and his scalp slightly, but not so well as to match the horse in the art. These muscles in man, because they are less useful and less efficient, are therefore said by the evolutionists to be "vestigial" muscles, muscles that we human beings could and did once use, when we were creatures of a lower order, but cannot now use because we have evolved. Some day, according to the theory, these muscles and others of the face will be entirely gone.

But, let us consider, why, on the theory of creation, man should be made so as to be able to twitch his skin and move his ears as vigorously as the horse. Man has a mind that serves him better than any set of muscles. Let us further ask if, when the time comes that these so-called useless muscles will be gone, we shall not be as dead in facial expression and appearance as stones. We shall be able neither to laugh nor smile, to raise our eyebrows nor otherwise express the personality within us. Finally, it must be considered, if the muscles that connect with our ears and enable us to move them as we do were ever absent entirely, would not something else be necessary to fill up the holes in the head caused by their absence? If these parts are useful only for filling in, they are not "vestigial."

We might refer in this connection to the so-called rudimentary "third eyelid" in man. Reptiles, birds, cats, all vertebrate animals, in fact, have fastened to the edge of the eye on one side a thin membrane that helps to hold the eye in place in the head. In some creatures this mem-

43

brane is so well developed that it is useful for cleaning off the eyeball. In man's eye, next to the nose, as the reader can see by inspection, there is a fold of whitish membrane that serves to fill in that corner of the eye and forms a delicate socket in which the eyeball turns. This fold is said to be "vestigial," a proof that man is a direct descendant of the reptiles! However, since the Creator used a common pattern, why should not this fold be there? What would take its place if it were gone?

It is hoped that the above discussion will suggest how to deal with a certain class of "evidences."

There are others, however, that should be taken up separately, among them certain so-called vestigial organs in the lower animals. The two most commonly mentioned are the "relics of rear legs" in whales, which are said to prove that whales are descendants of land animals, and the "relics of legs" in the great snake, the python or boa, which are said to prove that these serpents once walked.

In the rear part of the whale, about midway between the front paddles and the tail flukes by which the creature drives itself through the water, imbedded in the flesh of that region, are certain cartilaginous bones from six to ten inches in length. These bones are not connected with the spine, but are imbedded in the muscles. They do not approach the outside of the skin but are clearly an interior organ of the whale. These bones, existing in the whale in the general region where rear legs, if they existed, would be, are pointed to by the upholders of the evolutionary theory as evidence that the whale was once a land animal in possession of useful rear legs.

Before discussing the actual facts of the case it is well to consider what this "proof" calls upon men to accept. Evolutionists are wont to ridicule the creationists with being credulous, superstitious, able-to-believe-anything. To accept this proof means that one must believe that the whale came out of the water where it had been a fish, became a land animal, worked for millions of years to get legs, got them, used them, perhaps to climb trees with or gallop over the dusty plains, then got tired of being a land animal, began to live near the edge of the water, turned its front legs into paddles, developed tail-flukes to act as propellers, let its rear legs hang uselessly behind until they wasted away, and finally came to exist only in the state it is in today! Does not such a course of evolution cause one to wonder at the statement of President McMurrich of the University of Toronto, "It seems incredible that man as a reasoning animal can presume to doubt evolution"?

As said above, the whale is a mammal. The Creator made it, internally, not after the pattern of the fish, though it lives in the water, but after the pattern of the four-footed land animals. The pattern was modified, so as to substitute tail-flukes for rear legs. It was necessary, however, to provide certain bones in the rear part of the great monster to help support the mass of organs in that part. These bones were put there by the Creator and muscles attached to them by which the genital and other parts of the creature are supported. Having, thus, an important function these often mentioned bones in the whale are not vestigial anythings.[37]

The other so-called vestigial organs of the lower animals to be considered are the leg-bones of the boa. In the rear part of this great serpent there are two strong spurs [38] which project two or three inches. They are the visible parts of what are actually legs, the larger part of which are concealed under the skin. But the skin is very loose and pliable in that region and the legs can be moved vigorously back and forth. By means of the spurs the serpent, which kills by wrapping itself around its victim and squeezing it to death, can cut severe gashes by powerful, quick strokes. By means of the spurs it assists in propelling its great bulk along the ground. In view of the useful advantages the creature has in the possession of these spurs the leg-bones cannot be considered useless appendages.

We come now to the so-called vestigial organs in man besides those already mentioned: the tonsils, the thyroid

---

[37] See article, "Whale," in the *Cent. Dict. and Ency.*, 1911 ed.

[38] See picture and discussion in Ditmar's *Reptiles of the World*, pages 197, 218.

gland, the thymus gland, the pineal gland, the pituitary gland, and the vermiform appendix. Belief in evolution was given tremendous impulse until comparatively recent times by the oft repeated statements of evolutionists that the above mentioned organs of the human body were without rhyme or reason and could be dispensed with at any time. Medical science was then in a rather crude state. Today, because of the great progress of investigation in the study of human anatomy, evolutionists are strangely silent on all these once so-called "vestigial" organs. As Paley declared, "our list of useless structures decreases as our store of knowledge increases."

The once loudly proclaimed useless part, the thyroid gland, is now known to be vitally important in normal body growth. Improper functioning of the organ causes that hideous deformity called cretinism.[39] The thyroid controls the iodine that comes into the system in the food that is eaten. Yet this important part, because its function was unknown, was until quite recently an infallible "proof" of evolution. Another "vestigial" part, whose lack of function has been disproved, is the pituitary gland. On the functioning of this gland depends the proper growth of the skeleton. Over-activity of the gland causes abnormal growth. The giants which we see in circuses are probably victims of an over-activity of pituitary functions.[40] The pineal gland, another once infallible "proof," exerts its chief functional activity in childhood. "Until the seventh year this organ exerts an inhibitory influence upon the development of the sexual glands." [41] The function of the thymus is now clearly known. *It is an endocrine gland working with the thyroid.* Four pairs of lymphatic tissues exist in the upper human throat, one of which ordinary people call their "tonsils," although all four pairs are their tonsils. These are "a chain of fortresses protecting the body against invasion by pathogenic organisms." [42] In other words, the tonsils help to prevent disease germs from

---

[39] See *Thyroid and Thymus Gland,* 2nd ed., page 21, by Clinic of George W. Crile and Associates.

[40] See *The Endocrines,* by S. Wyllis Bandler, pages 100-104.

[41] See ibid., page 93.

[42] *A Laboratory Textbook of Human Anatomy,* by O. F. Kampmeier, 1944, page 128, part VII.

entering the system. They are especially important in children. Concerning the thymus and the tonsils, Sir Arthur Keith, head of the Royal College of Surgeons, London, said, "no one would describe them as vestiges." [43]

The following concerning that notorious "proof" of evolution, the appendix, is from a member of the faculty of one of the large medical schools of America: "Both the tonsils and the appendix are largely composed of lymphoid tissue. The function of lymphoid tissue, wherever it is found, is intimately related to combatting the invasion of the body by foreign agents, particularly bacteria. The tonsils and appendix engage in this protective function, consequently they can not be thought of as inert or vestigial tissues from this point of view. The appendix, in addition to being a lymph organ, also happens to be an extension of the large intestine. Because of its narrow lumen (or duct) . . . it is difficult to conceive how the appendix can play a significant role in the digestion and absorption of foodstuffs. From this point of view, i.e., as an organ important in the handling of foodstuffs, it may be considered rudimentary in the human species, but it must be remembered that it still contains its lymph structure and functions in much the same manner as its parent, the larger intestine." The member of the faculty of the medical school thus quoted then refers to the author of a text-book of human anatomy [44] who says, "The designation 'abdominal tonsil' . . . is sometimes applied to the appendix . . . (which) is found only in scattered forms of mammals: in the wombat, rabbit, some lemurs, in anthropoid apes, and in man. It is erroneously classed as a vestigial organ." Keith likewise says [45] that the appendix "does not merit the name 'vestigial' " and says that in growth and atrophy in later years the appendix keeps company with other lymphatic glands of the body.

Attention is called to the presence of the appendix in lower animals. If, as was once said, the appendix is a "vestigial" organ in man because its function is unknown,

[43] *Nature,* Dec. 12, 1925.
[44] Kampmeier, O. F., *A Laboratory Textbook of Human Anatomy,* 1944, p. 405, part IV.
[45] *Nature,* Dec. 12, 1925.

then evolution has produced a totally useless organ in the entire animal world, because no more is known about its function in the lower animals than in man. Furthermore, it is odd that the appendix should exist in what are said to be man's closest relatives, the higher apes, but not in his less immediate relatives, the monkeys, and yet should appear again in animals farther down the scale, e.g., the rabbit, wombat and opossum.[46]*

It might be well to add a word in connection with so-called vestigial organs regarding the reputed existence of human beings with "tails." Every now and then it is reported that a baby has been born with a tail, or a tailed family has been discovered somewhere, usually in some far away corner of the earth. It is rather significant that when such cases are reported the descriptions of them are so meager, or the time of their occurrence so remote that one who might wish to make a personal investigation would not be able to do so. All reports of human tails, however apparently authoritative, should be received with suspicion. Zeal to establish their theory will sometimes lead evolutionists to accept and report cases that are totally without foundation. As a proof of this, what occurred a few years ago may be cited. Dr. W. W. Keen, a man of reputation in evolutionary circles, wrote a book called *"I Believe in God and in Evolution"* in which he published a faked picture of a man with a tail. When the fact that the photograph was faked was called to his attention he wrote to the magazine *Science* as follows: "In my book, *'I Believe in God and in Evolution,'* I have included in the fourth edition a photograph of an Igorot with a tail, which I vouched for, as I understood that it had been photographed by my own grandson, Mr. John Freeman. A few days ago within a few hours of each other, I received letters from Dr. Alex Hrdlicka, of the division of physical anthropology of the National Museum of the Smithsonian Institute and from Mrs. Ella F. Grave, who a year ago had been doing some work in the Philippines for the National Research Council. Both of these correspondents stated that the Bureau of Science in Manila had shown them the original of this

[46] Mivart, *Man and Apes,* page 161.
*See Appendix III, Section 1, page 196.

photograph which showed it was a fake photograph, the tail having been added to the original by the photographer, I suppose as a joke. On communicating with my grandson I find that I misinterpreted his letter and that he did not photograph this Igorot." Keen then went on to say that his mistake did not mean that human tails do not prove man's animal ancestry, "for there are plenty of genuine tails." In a later communication to the same magazine he stated that "two new photographs, unquestionably authentic" had been substituted for the faked one, one photograph of a case reported in 1901, the other in 1889. It is doubtful, however, if many will agree that the new photographs are "unquestionably authentic" after the publication of the faked one, which was also once to be relied on as authentic.[47]

Aside from falsely reported cases of actual human tails what may happen is this: As students of embryology know, injuries or accidents are likely to occur in embryonic development which cause freaks of nature. Among animals two-headed calves and cats and puppies, and in the human family three-legged men and two persons with a common stomach have been born. Evolutionists do not contend that therefore there have been such ancestors as these for animals and men. In like manner injuries have occurred in the development of the human embryo which have caused the coccyx or lower end of the spine to be abnormally developed, thus giving the suggestion of a tail. This does not mean that men had tailed ancestors any more than two-headed calves prove that modern cattle are descended from two-headed cattle.

Monstrosities due to accidents in very early stages of individual development, rather than the evolution of the whole human race, account for some so-called proofs of evolution, such as the very rare births of men or women with supernumerary breasts. A rather common condition, in which men's second and third toes are joined, may well be a condition which is of genetic origin, i. e., one Divinely provided for at creation, like white streaks of hair above the forehead, rather than be a condition due to man's

---

[47] *Science,* April 2, 1926, and June 11, 1926.

evolution from webbed bird or reptile ancestors, as some evolutionists have maintained.

Much has been made by evolutionists of the fact that very young infants can support their weight by their fingers at an early age, this being a sign, it is said, of man's arboreal ancestry. It is to be explained, however, by the fact that infants possess this ability because they have been very active in the womb in opening and closing their fingers, and have thus developed strong hand muscles. Where the will to believe in evolution exists there exists also the willingness to grasp at any straw which may seem to support that theory.

Fig. 13. What we use for fans today. Fossil palm-leaf from the "Cretaceous epoch." The reason no leaves of this kind are ever found in what the evolutionists call "early" (Paleozoic) layers of earth is because the evolutionists themselves do all the naming of the rocks and they never permit a layer in which such leaves are found to be called early. The evolutionary biologist tells the geologist that palms are a "higher" or complex form of plant life and must therefore have evolved late in the process of evolution. Consequently the geologist says that whatever earth-layer a palm may be found in must be a late deposit, and he puts that layer somewhere near the top of the geologic column, regardless of its actual position in nature. (Fossil from U. S. G. S. Pro. Paper 101.)

51

THE "PROOF" FROM GEOLOGY

What is considered by many evolutionists as the strongest proof of evolution is now to be considered.

Throughout the world in many places there are known to be rock-layers of various thicknesses lying horizontally one upon another. These layers, or "strata," as they are also called, can often be seen along railroad cuts and river banks. The horizontal deposits were evidently made by the agency of water. Those that are lowest in the earth were deposited first, those on the top deposited last.

The evolutionists say that these layers of rock were deposited thus through periods of hundreds of millions of years. The first to be deposited, they say, was laid down almost a billion years ago. The latest is being de-

Fig. 14. Leaf of a living *hickory* compared with the leaf of a *hickory* from the so-called Pliocene epoch. Fossil from United States Geological Survey Professional Paper 98

posited today. And all through the intervening ages deposits were being made.

Furthermore, the evolutionists say, during the immense periods when these deposits were being made, living things were evolving upon the earth. Starting with some

Fig. 15. Leaf of a living *Japanese* oak compared with a leaf of a fossil *Japanese* oak from the so-called Eocene age. Fossil from United States Geological Survey Professional Paper 91

very simple form, life changed and developed until man and all the host of plants and animals of today were produced. And, evolutionists say, these developing forms left records of their evolution through the ages in the layers of soil that were deposited contemporaneously with them. Consequently, in the lowest strata are found as fossils the simplest forms of life, those which were evolved first, while in the top or most recently deposited layers are found the most complex forms, the forms of life last to be evolved.

It is the statement, therefore, in substance, that the deeper down into the earth we dig the simpler and stranger will be the forms of fossil-life discovered, until we come to a place where no traces of past life exist, which constitutes the geological argument for evolution.

Fig. 16. Leaf of a living *walnut* compared with the leaf of a *walnut* from the so-called Cretaceous age. Fossil from United States Geological Professional Paper 101

The criticism of this "proof" from the creationist's point of view is so ample and varied that it will be considered under the following heads:

1. *Do the fossils themselves show this evolution, or are they essentially the same as corresponding forms today?*

Granting, for the time being, that some fossil forms are many millions of years old, the fact remains that those that have living representatives, no matter how old they are, are the same in appearance as living forms. The world in which we live is, as it has been called, "a zoologically impoverished" world, by which is meant a world which has no longer the large numbers of species with which it was once stocked. Of those that were created a considerable portion have been unable to withstand the rigors and hardships that a changed condition [48] in the world has produced, and have ceased to exist. But those

Fig. 17. Leaf of a living *grape* compared with the leaf of a *grape* from the so-called Cretaceous age. Fossil from United States Geological Survey Professional Paper 101.

which have survived correspond exactly with those of their kind whose remains have been unearthed as fossils.

In 1938 deep-water fishermen, who were fishing off the coast of South Africa, brought to the surface a fighting, threshing fish five feet long and a hundred and twenty-seven pounds in weight, such as they had never seen before. Scientists, being called in to investigate, called it a Coelacanth (Fig. 18), identical in every respect with the Coelacanths whose fossils are found in considerable numbers buried in the strata of the United States, Germany, and elsewhere. These strata are said by evolu-

[48] The Deluge offers to the believer in the Bible a likely point in world history when the changed condition began.

tionary geologists to have been formed in the Triassic Age, or "Age of Reptiles," and the Coelacanths whose fossils these strata contain are said to have become extinct "90,000,000 years ago." [49]

Fig. 18. *Above*, photo of a living Coelacanth caught in a net in very deep water off the coast of South Africa in December, 1938. *Below*, photo of a fossil Coelacanth from the "Triassic" strata of Germany, said to agree in every detail with the living Coelacanth.

[49] *Life*, April 3, 1939; *Time*, April 3, 1939. Some geologists place the Triassic Age at 400,000,000 years ago. A second fish of the Coelacanth species was caught near Madagascar in December, 1952.

In the so-called oldest rocks, those supposed to be always deepest down in the earth, the "Paleozoic," there are fossil remains of star-fish, which, when compared with living forms, are found to be essentially the same. (Fig. 21). In spite of supposed hundreds of millions of years of evolution the present star-fish, corals, and crinoids of our modern seas are still today easily recognized as the same creatures as their remote ancestors.

Fig. 19. Leaf of a living *magnolia* compared with the leaf of a *magnolia* from the so-called Cretaceous age. Fossil from United States Geological Survey Professional Paper 101.

In those "ancient" rocks, also, are found various kinds of fishes that have their exact counter-parts in living fishes of today. The so-called Devonian rocks of Ohio, extending entirely across the state, contain fish remains in great numbers, chiefly sharks, of which it has been said that

57

Fig. 20. *Ginko* or Maiden hair leaves from the "Jurassic Epoch" compared with leaves of the living *Ginko*. Living leaves from one tree. Fossils from United States Geological Survey Professional Paper 85.

their jaws and teeth "were established essentially as at present." [50] In the group of layers called "Mesozoic," which are supposed to contain the remains of those creatures that came into existence midway through the long

[50] J. E. Hyde in *Natural History Magazine,* Sept.-Oct., 1926, page 500.

Fig. 21. *Above* are varieties of star-fish as they exist today. *(Smithsonian Institute Bulletin* 100). *Below* are varieties of star-fish found as fossils in so-called "Ordovician Rocks." *(Smithsonian Institute Bulletin* 88). Three quarters of a billion years are said to separate the living from the fossil types. There is no essential difference between them. How is this persistency of species to be accounted for?

period of supposed evolution, there are remains of plants of various kinds (Fig. 14, 15, 16, 17, 19, 20)—laurel leaves, oak leaves, willow leaves, beech and alder leaves—which, by all the straining in the world, cannot but be called by the names by which their living representatives are known. Though the trees have had, according to the theory, at least a hundred million years in which to change, they are readily identified as ancestors of the living forms. When we come down to the fossils of only a supposed ten million years ago, the period called "Tertiary," we find that the creatures of that day—pigs, elephants, tigers, bears, apes, are similar in type to living forms. All of which points to the truth of the Biblical principle that living things have brought forth *after their kind.*

To impress the reader with this persistence of types as shown by the geological record we can do no better than to quote the famous evolutionist, Thomas Huxley, "If we confine ourselves to positively ascertained facts, the total amount of change in the forms of animals and vegetable life, since existence of such forms is recorded, is small. When compared with the lapse of time since the first appearance of these forms, the amount of change is wonderfully small. Moreover, in each great group of the animal and vegetable kingdom there are certain forms which I termed persistent types which have remained with but little apparent change from their first appearance to the present time." [51] And we might add the following quotation from a more recent geologist, "Perhaps the first and most obvious lesson to be gleaned from the study of fossils is the elementary truth that life, even in the earliest times, differed in no way from the life of today. Further, we observe that the lowly types of life that appear in the oldest rocks have persisted through all geological times up to the present day." [52]

2. *Do the fossils reveal the transition stages that the geological "proof" requires?*

If throughout past ages life was actually drifting over in one continual stream from one form into another, it is

---

[51] *Critiques and Addresses,* page 182.
[52] Prof. James Park, *Textbook of Geology,* page 265 (1925).

to be expected that as many samples of the intermediate stages between species should be discovered in fossil condition as of the species themselves. According to the theory invertebrates gradually turned into fishes, fishes gradually

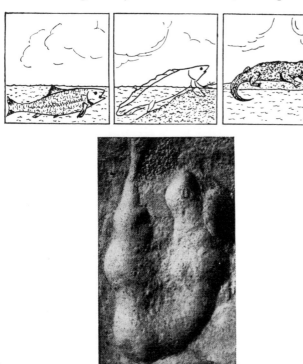

Fig. 22 — Missing links exist not only between men and apes but in many other places along the supposed line of evolution. *Above* is the theoretical line of evolution from fish to land animals. Fossil fish (left) in great numbers are found. Fossil amphibians — lizards, salamanders, crocodiles (right) in great numbers are found. But few, if any, transition forms (center) are found, although they ought to exist in as great a number as either fish or amphibians, if evolution has taken place.

Below is a photograph and what was said about it by a noted evolutionist, H. F. Osborn, Director of the New York Museum of Natural History: "A single impression of a three-toed footprint in the Upper Devonian Shales of Pennsylvania constitute at present (1925) the sole paleontological proof of the long period of transition of the vertebrates from the fish type to the amphibian type." Lull describes this impression as "baffling in its obscurity." The reader can readily agree. Footprint illustration and quotation are from Osborn's *Origin and Evolution of Life*, page 176, 7. By permission.

became four-legged amphibians, amphibians drifted over into reptiles. Reptiles with scales gradually transformed their scales into feathers and their front feet into bird's wings, while other reptiles slowly transformed themselves into fur-bearing quadrupeds. The quadrupeds in turn drifted over gradually into apes, and apes drifted in herds over into men. If these things actually happened, it is certainly fair to suppose that we should find vast numbers of the drifting-over forms. There is no reason why we should not. It is difficult to imagine why there should be definite, fixed types such as we find in the fossil world at all. All should be in a state of flux. But these missing links are wanting. There are no fossils of creatures whose scales were changing into feathers or whose feet were changing into wings, no fossils of fish getting legs (Fig. 22) or of reptiles getting hair. The real task of the geological evolutionist is not to find "the" missing link, as if there were only one. The task is to find those thousands upon thousands of missing links that connect the many fossil species with one another. The lack of transition forms described above is acknowledged by Prof. T. D. A. Cockerell of the University of Colorado in the following words, "There are *innumerable* 'missing-links' in all groups, and we can never hope to complete the history of life from fossil remains."[53] The existence of these gaps is further testified to by Dr. Austin H. Clark of the United States National Museum, whose statements in 1929 caused a furor in evolutionary camps, where it was felt that he was giving the case away. The theory of evolution is that an original, primitive cell slowly and gradually branched out into all modern forms of life like so many branches of a tree. This view, Clark says, must be modified, for, says he, "gaps are found in all these evolutionary lines, and many of these gaps appear to be real—that is, they were never, so far as we have been able to learn, bridged by so-called missing-links. To take a concrete example, it is quite obvious that the gap between cats and dogs is broad, and it remains broad throughout the fossil record. Cats never became dogs, nor dogs cats; but both are carnivorous mammals. Be-

[53] *Zoology,* page 140.

tween the backbones in animals and the invertebrates the gaps are very wide, and those peculiar types which are intermediate between them are widely different from either. Between the various invertebrate groups, as the arthropods, echinoderms, nemerteans, and so forth, the gaps are still wider. Indeed, so broad are the gaps between these various types of lower animals that they can not be arranged in any sort of evolutionary line. . . . The gaps between the various invertebrate phyla go back quite unchanged to the very earliest fossils that are adequately known, those of Cambrian time." [54]

The above gives the gist of Clark's view of missing-links. He is of the evolutionary school, however, and the way he manages to reconcile these gaps with evolution is to hold that, in some unaccountable way, great leaps were made in the evolutionary process, such that widely differing forms suddenly appeared without any transition steps at all. In later pages of this book the matter of "mutations" will be discussed, a process by which new varieties within species are at present being produced —new forms of dogs among dogs, new forms of poppies among poppies. The mutations or leaps which Clark maintains have occurred are not of this order, but far greater. There is nothing in nature now to which we can compare them.

A late [1938] acknowledgement of the lack of transitional forms comes from Prof. Caullery of the Chair of Evolution of the University of Paris: "The general fact that paleontology shows us few transitional forms, and still fewer primitive forms is very disturbing." [55]

3. *The "imperfection" of the geological record.*

The manner in which the absence of connecting links among the fossils is accounted for is seen in the following quotation from Charles Darwin, "Geology assuredly does not reveal any such finely-graded organic chain; and this perhaps is the most obvious and serious objection which can be urged against the theory. The explanation lies, however, in the extreme imperfection of the geological

---

[54] *Science,* March 8, 1929.
[55] *Science,* 1938.

record." [56] It should be noted where this great champion puts the blame when conditions are not right for the theory which he made famous.

Imperfection as an excuse for the absence of links, however, leaves a dangerous hole in the geological argument. If the record is so imperfect that the necessary connecting links are not found, what assurance can the evolutionists give that the same imperfection does not hide more important facts—such, for example, as that horses lived in the "age of reptiles" and apes in the "age of fishes"? If the record is imperfect, how do they know that the bones of such "higher" types of animals as deer or pigs will not some day be found in strata supposed to have been deposited millions of years before those types were evolved? How do they know that the remains of the modern horse will not be found in a so-called "Cretaceous" stratum (Cretaceous strata being the deposits supposed to have been made when reptilian forms were ruling the world as the highest forms of life)? If the record is imperfect they do not know, and therefore horses may have roved in one part of the earth in "Cretaceous" time while reptiles lived in another part. Apes may have lived as early as the "Devonian" age, the so-called "age of fishes." Bateson pointed to this hole in the geological "proof" when he said to the assembled scientists of America, "It has been asked how we know that there were no mammals (e. g. rabbits, sheep, horses) in the Paleozoic time. May there not have been mammals somewhere on the earth, though no vestige of them has come down to us?" [57]

Of course, mammals will never be found in "Paleozoic" strata—not for very long. Of that we are absolutely positive for this reason: Mammals did not live in "Paleozoic" time (i e. when fishes are supposed to have been the most advanced form of life) according to the evolutionists. Mammals evolved later. If remains of any mammal should ever be found in a layer that had previously been called "Paleozoic," the evolutionists would say a mistake had been made, and the age-name would be changed. Such renaming of strata has been done again

[56] *Origin of Species*, volume 2, page 49, 6th ed.
[57] *Science*, Jan. 20, 1922

and again in the last seventy-five years, and the evolutionists now have the strata labelled about as they want. [58]
The evolutionary labellers of the rocks simply will not let
things get out of order for their theory, and to keep the
order right an astonishing method is sometimes used, i. e.
the order of the strata is said to have been reversed (See
Fig. 23).

No one need expect that such a thing—a mammal
being found in "Paleozoic" rock or a horse in "Cretaceous"—will ever occur so long as the evolutionists are in
control of the labelling of the rocks. The creationists,
however, should know the reason. Which leads to the
question:

4. *Is one fossil necessarily any older than any other?*
May not the vast majority of plants and animals whose
remains have been unearthed have lived and been destroyed at the same time? We touch here upon the very
vitals of the proof from geology.

The evolutionists say that the simplest forms of life
(corals, star-fish, crinoids) are very old, and the very
complex forms (bears, elephants, camels) are very young,
the former being several hundreds of millions of years
old, the latter being only five or ten millions of years old.
The youngest have evolved out of the oldest. These statements are made on the basis of the supposed fact that the
simplest forms (corals, star-fish) are found in the lowest
layers of earth, and the most complex forms found in the
highest layers.

Is this, however, always the case? In the fossil world
are the simplest forms always found at the bottom and
the complex structures at the top? In other words, are
corals, crinoids, star-fish—forms of life supposed to have

---

[58] The evolutionary rule governing the designation of the age
of strata is this: if a deposit contains the remains of several forms,
as many do, some higher and some lower in the evolutionary scale,
the higher form gives the age to the strata. To illustrate: if a
snake and a horse and a turtle are found as fossils in a stratum
the horse is the form that gives the age to the stratum. As long
as remains of turtles and snakes alone are found in a rock that
rock might be called "Cretaceous." If later a fossil horse is found
with the turtle and snake, the age of the rock is changed to "Ter
tiary."

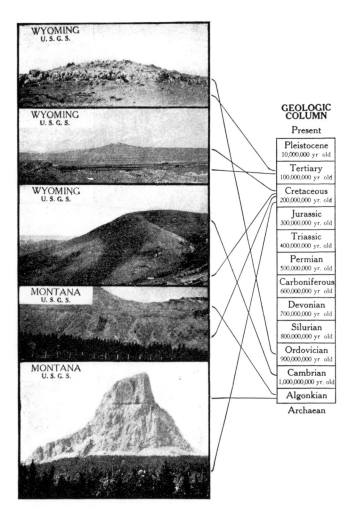

Fig. 23. "We may even demonstrate that strata have turned completely upside down if we can show that fossils in what are the uppermost layers ought properly to lie underneath those in the beds below them." Sir Archibald Giekie, *Textbook of Geology*, p. 837. The regions of the earth's surface pictured above, which are but a few of hundreds of similar examples, are parts of areas thousands of square

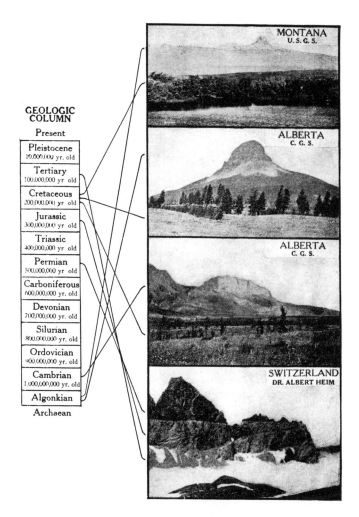

GEOLOGIC COLUMN

Present

Pleistocene 10,000,000 yr. old
Tertiary 100,000,000 yr old
Cretaceous 200,000,000 yr old
Jurassic 300,000,000 yr old
Triassic 400,000,000 yr old
Permian 500,000,000 yr old
Carboniferous 600,000,000 yr. old
Devonian 700,000,000 yr. old
Silurian 800,000,000 yr. old
Ordovician 900,000,000 yr. old
Cambrian 1,000,000,000 yr. old
Algonkian

Archaean

MONTANA
U. S. G. S.

ALBERTA
C. G. S.

ALBERTA
C. G. S.

SWITZERLAND
DR. ALBERT HEIM

miles in extent which have been "demonstrated" to have "turned completely upside down," because, forsooth, the most complex fossils are at the bottom and the most simple at top. Evolutionists say there are "faults" here. The "faults" are not evident in the mountainous regions themselves. The real fault is in the paper column, built upon an assumed evolution, in the center.

67

been the first to appear in the evolutionary process—never found in earth-layers that are *above* those containing fishes and reptiles—forms of life supposed to have evolved later? The answer is yes, they are. The order of superposition in which fossils are found is very often *upside-down* for the theory of evolution. Such upside-down areas are known in China, Norway, the Alps, Scotland, New York, Tennessee, Georgia, Idaho, Montana, Alberta and elsewhere and they extend in some instances for thousands of square miles. Where such embarrassing conditions exist, and prove, according to the evidence of superposition, such interesting things as that great monster reptiles became tiny sponges, corals, and trilobites,[59] the evolutionist has an explanation to offer that puts the blame upon innocent Nature, and makes her, instead of the theory he upholds, the deceiver. It is said by him that wherever the order of the fossil-bearing layers are in reverse to that which the theory of evolution demands there have been great cataclysms of nature, i. e., monster thrusts or tremendous folds of the strata, whereby thousands of square miles have risen up somehow out of the earth and slid or turned over so that they now lie perfectly horizontally, the top on the bottom and the bottom on the top. Where such things have occurred it is said that the earth has a "fault."

For the full consideration of the attempted evolutionary explanations of the manner in which these griddle-cake stunts of nature have occurred the reader will have to turn to other books on the subject.[60] Suffice it to be said here that areas of 20,000 square miles or more are involved in the "faults" in nature which have gotten evolutionary geologists into such great difficulties. Further, it should be known, in the regions where these things are said to have occurred there is no real evidence whatever that any great disturbance of normal conditions has ever

---

[59] In Montana and Alberta over a vast territory reptile-bearing "Cretaceous" rocks *underlie* trilobite "Paleozoic" rocks (Fig. 24).

[60] For a full account of the absence of a true chronological sequence in the fossil containing earth-layers *The New Geology* and *Evolutionary Geology and the New Catastrophism* by George McCready Price are recommended, also the author's *Deluge Story in Stone*.

taken place. Layers of earth containing "lower" organisms lie *perfectly naturally* on top of layers that contain "higher" forms. (See Fig. 23, 24.)

5. *Is not the argument from geology mere reasoning in a circle?* The fact of the matter is that such is the case. Modern historical geology is built on the *assumption* of evolution. The earth has been compelled by evolutionists to testify the way their theory requires.

In the middle of the last century certain geologists were told by biologists that evolution was an established fact. The geologists believed what they heard, and, believing, began to make an arrangement of the earth-strata on paper so as to conform to the supposed historical fact of evolution. If a layer of earth were discovered which contained fossils of plants and animals said by the biologists to have evolved first, that layer was put at the bottom of their paper diagram, regardless of the actual position in nature. If a layer were discovered which contained fossils of plants and animals which the biologist told them were evolved last, they put that layer at the top, regardless of its actual physical position. Thus, by ignoring upside-down conditions in nature, by describing them as "deceptions," and by concocting impossible explanations of how tremendous areas come to be upside-down, the geological evolutionists got up a "geologic column" based entirely on the assumption that evolution was a fact. Historical geology rests on evolutionary biology. It is an amusing spectacle today, therefore, to find evolutionary biologists, feeling the need of support for their theory, sometimes turning to historical geology for help. The evolutionary geologist and the evolutionary biologist today often present a picture of two men trying to sit on each other's shoulders.

To establish in the mind of the reader the fact that the above statements concerning the geological proof are true we will quote several foremost modern evolutionary geologists. *First,* in order to show that evolution is accepted by geologists on the basis of what they are told by biological evolutionists we will quote Grabau,[61] "That the modern animal and plant world has developed by

[61] *Textbook of Geology,* volume 2, page 53.

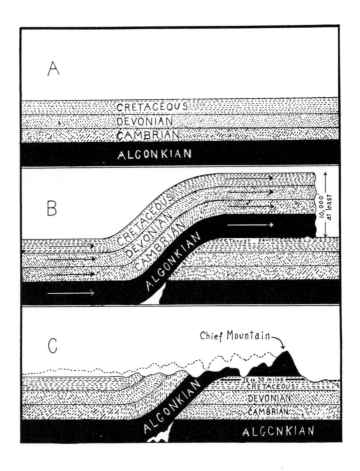

A

CRETACEOUS
DEVONIAN
CAMBRIAN
ALGONKIAN

B

CRETACEOUS
DEVONIAN
CAMBRIAN
ALGONKIAN

10,000' at least

THRUST FAULT

C

Chief Mountain

15 to 30 miles
CRETACEOUS
DEVONIAN
CAMBRIAN

ALGONKIAN

ALGONKIAN

Fig. 24. Diagram showing how the evolutionists explain the presence of "Paleozoic" rocks, which are supposed to have been deposited when life first began to evolve, on the top of "Cretaceous" rocks, which are supposed to have been deposited hundreds of millions of years later. A (opposite page) shows the situation as the evolutionists imagine it in Montana, Alberta. and British Columbia at the close of the "Cretaceous epoch." Only three of the Paleozoic series of deposits are represented in the diagram (Devonian, Cambrian, Algonkian). B illustrates the situation a little later as the evolutionists imagine it. For some reason the land to the west raised up from the depth of at least 10,000 feet and pushed over the land to the east, upon which, at the end of the shove or "thrust," it was lying horizontally. C illustrates the situation at the present time. During the millions of years that passed since the "thrust" occurred, the winds and rain carried away all the layers above the "Algonkian," leaving it exposed on top of the "Cretaceous." The area of the earth's surface in this region where the order of the fossil-containing-earths is upside-down for the theory of evolution, and where the "thrust" is said to have occurred, is 350 miles long and totals about 7,000 square miles.

All this is very clever. The trouble is that it is based merely on the necessity of accounting somehow for a natural condition of earth layers that is in opposition to what the proof of evolution from geology demands. The pushing of so enormous a mass and weight of rock over another mass could not but leave unmistakable evidence of its having done so in the form of cracks and broken fragments and disturbances of various kinds. Yet there is no such evidence. R. G. McConnel of the Canadian Geological Survey says that the upper, "Paleozoic" (Algonkian) rocks and the lower, "Cretaceous" rocks are *"nearly horizontal,"* and *"appear to succeed one another conformably."* (Annual Report, 1886, Part D.) This means, in geological parlance, according to Webster's Dictionary, that the "Paleozoic" layers lie on the "Cretaceous" as if both *"were formed by uninterrupted deposition under the same general conditions."* In other words, it appears as if the same action of water that deposited the sediment that became "Paleozoic" rock also deposited the sediment that became "Cretaceous" rock.

That the above explanation of this "upside-down" area is not thoroughly satisfactory to evolutionary geologists, although they have nothing better to offer, is revealed by the following statement by Prof. W. W. Watts, President of the Geology Section of the British Association for the Advancement of Science: "The problem of the overthrust 'nappes' (surfaces) of mountain regions is one of our greatest difficulties, and all explanations hitherto proposed are so *hopelessly inadequate* that we have sometimes felt compelled to doubt *whether the facts really are as stated* (i.e. upside-down). But the phenomena have now been observed so carefully and in so many different districts that any real doubt as to the facts is out of the question, and we must still look for some adequate method by which the over-thrusting could have been brought about." *(Smithsonian Institute Report, 1925, page 283.)*

To account for a more distressing situation which exists in the Alps (see Fig. 23) European evolutionary geologists have offered more wonderful explanations. They have published diagrams showing how the once level strata in that region, totalling ten thousand feet in thickness, pushed up many miles in the air and turned completely over, in the manner of a loose rug which has been folded by a kick, and were not broken in any manner. The "upside-down" strata in the Alps offer no evidence save that they were deposited just as they are and have never been disturbed. If creationists ever invented such explanations in order to maintain their views, the evolutionists would heap untold reproach and ridicule upon them.

71

natural methods from pre-existing simpler forms . . . has been *clearly demonstrated by the labours of biologists.*" Just how clearly it has been demonstrated has been shown in the preceding pages. *Second,* in order to show that geologists make evolution the basis of their geological history, we will quote Schuchert and Pirsson,[62] "The fundamental principle underlying all endeavor to make out the geological past is evolution." The same authors also say,[63] "After one hundred years of endeavor a great deal of knowledge has been worked out as to the evolutionary sequence of organisms, and this knowledge can be relied upon to *fix in turn the stratigraphical sequence* (relative order of the earthlayers)." *Third,* to show that if the natural order of the layers on the face of the earth is contrary to what the evolutionary hypothesis demands, the natural order is considered wrong, we will quote Nicholson,[64] who says that because of the assumed truth of evolution, "It may even be said that in any case where there should appear to be clear any decisive disordance between the physical (layer-order) and the paleontological (fossil) evidence as to the age of a given series of beds, it is *the former that is to be distrusted rather than the latter.*" On this point we also quote Geikie,[65] who says that because of the assumed fact that life has evolved on the earth, "We may even *demonstrate* that . . . strata have turned completely upside down if we can show that the fossils in what are now the uppermost layers *ought properly* to lie underneath those in the beds below them."

Having this information in mind it is not difficult to see the fault in all genealogies based on fossil remains, whether in whole, as from fish to man, or in part, as in the case of the horse. Definite reference may be made to the horse, since the ancestral line of man's domestic friend is claimed by evolutionists to be the best established of all genealogies based on paleontology. Fossils of five animals are found. These are of four extinct animals called respectively Eohippus, Protorohippus, Mesophippus,

---

[62] *Textbook of Geology,* volume 2, page 446.
[63] Volume 2, page 24.
[64] *Ancient Life History of the Earth,* page 40.
[65] *Textbook of Geology,* 1903 ed., page 837.

Protohippus, and the modern horse, Equus. The horse as we know it is found as a true fossil here in America, where it was extinct when Columbus discovered the land. There is no difference whatever in the manner in which these animals (including the horse) exist as fossils. The places in which they are found are widely scattered, hundreds of miles apart, and the strata in which the fossils are found are surface strata. One fossil is not found below the other in any sense of the word. For all geological evidence there is to the contrary all the animals mentioned may have lived and died at the same time. Yet names are given to the rocks in which the fossils are found suggesting different ages (Eocene, Oligocene, Miocene, Pliocene, Pleistocene, Recent), and the fossils themselves are arranged in a series from the smallest, Eohippus, a four-toed creature about the size of a fox, up to the largest, the modern single-toed horse, and people are told that this is the time order in which they lived, and that this is the line of ancestry of the horse.[66]

In the "proof" of evolution from geology old mother Earth is thus coached, nay even brow-beaten, to testify for evolution. A forced witness is not a good one.

6. *How, in the light of Revelation, can conditions of the fossils and the natural relative orders of the earth's strata be accounted for?*

Up until the early part of the nineteenth century the existence of fossils was explained on the basis of the Biblical Deluge. (See the author's *The Deluge Story in Stone—A History of the Flood Theory of Geology*. Augsburg Publishing House, 1931.) With the rise of the modern evolutionary "theory of uniformity," i. e., that nature's ways have always been calm and slow, came the doctrine

---

[66] Osborn's genealogy of the horse has been the basis of this discussion. Another authority, Marsh, gives the horse a somewhat different line of ancestors. According to all genealogies the horse began as a four-toed animal. Coming from a reptile it was once even a five-toed animal. The horse in an early stage of embryological development should, therefore, "recapitulate" that stage and show the five toes well developed. It does not. Which, therefore, is wrong, paleontology or embryology? Nor does the whale, which was once a four-footed land animal, according to theory, ever in embryological development have four legs.

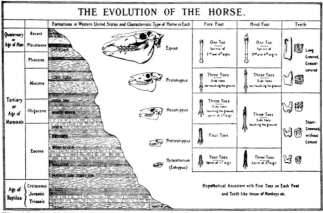

Fig. 25. A deceptive diagram. According to this drawing it appears as if "Hyracotherium" (Eohippus), the smallest animal at the bottom, was geologically much older than Equus (our common horse), the largest animal at the top, and that therefore "Hyracotherium" must have evolved into Equus through a long period of time. It must be remembered, however, that geology itself does not show that "Hyracotherium" is older than Equus. For all that geology proves to the contrary, both animals may have been living side by side, or at the same time in different parts of the world, since the Wasatch formation (see diagram) in which the fossils of "Hyracotherium" are found is a surface formation of the earth, found in Idaho, and the Sheridan formation in which fossils of the true horses are found is also a surface formation of the earth, found in Nebraska. Neither formation can be clearly said to be older than the other. For all that the evolutionists know about the matter, the Wasatch formation and the Sheridan formation may have been deposited at nearly the same time, not one million of years before the other as their theory requires. These things show how much the 'proofs' of evolution are nothing but assumptions. Evolution is first assumed to be true; a scheme is then made up to conform to that assumption; then the scheme is used to show that evolution is true.

that all the past changes upon the earth were made not by great, physical forces working fast and violently as in a Deluge, but calmly through long ages. Evolutionists assume, without proof, that events have never occurred in the past in a different manner from that in which they are occurring now. Only present laws have ever been in operation, they say. The Flood, however, still remains a challenging explanation of conditions as they are found in the earth. Certain respects in which the Deluge readily accounts for the conditions in nature may be mentioned.

Nowhere on the earth is there any considerable number of fossils being formed today. Leaves falling from the trees rot away quickly. Rarely, under modern "uniform conditions," are they buried in such a way as to form a fossil. Yet, in many places the world over, leaves of trees, vines, ferns and palms are unearthed in the greatest numbers and in the most wonderful state of preservation. Many parts of the so-called "Cretaceous" and "Tertiary" rock are fairly jammed full with marvelous preserved leaf fossils. The coal-beds of the "Carboniferous" strata are composed of the pressed remains of tree-ferns, whose modern representatives make up a large part of the tropical forests of today. These buried tree-ferns have left their beautiful leafy imprints in millions of chunks of coal. Coal-beds of other "ages," e. g. the "Cretaceous," and "Tertiary" are composed of such plant remains as sassafras, laurel, magnolia, poplar, willow, maple, birch, beech and elm, showing flowers and fruits in a marvelous state of preservation—as the great geologist Dana has said, "with all the perfection they have in a herbarium." Coal is undoubtedly a catastrophic formation, not a "peat-bog" formation as the evolutionists say. No "peat-bog" theory can account for the way many coal layers on top of one another, some thick and some as thin as a sheet of paper, are spread out in horizontal and parallel layers over an area many thousands of square miles, as in Pennsylvania, West Virginia, Kentucky and Tennessee. Only a flood-like action of some sort can do that.

Fish, when they die under modern uniform conditions, immediately come to the surface of the water, float with stomach up, begin to decompose within a few hours, and fall apart bit by bit. Yet the hardened strata of the earth in all continents contain literally millions of fish buried in whole shoals in a perfect state of preservation. Miners in Wallace, Idaho, dig out again and again from deep down in the earth the most perfectly kept fish forms. Hugh Miller, in *The Old Red Sandstone*,[67] describes fully the fish fossils as they are found in Scotland. He says that over an area of ten thousand square miles fish remains are found bearing "unequivocably the marks of violent death. The figures are contorted, contracted, curved, the tail in many instances is bent around to the head, the spines stick out, the fins are spread to the full" as fish would be which were dying as earth sediment, stirred up from the surfaces

[67] Page 221.

75

of the continents by the Flood, settled thicker and heavier upon them. William Buckland [68] thus describes the petrified fish found in the Alps: "They are always entire, and so closely packed on one another that many individuals are often contained in a single block. All these fish must have died suddenly on this fatal spot, and have been buried speedily in the sediment then in the course of deposition. From the fact that certain individuals have even preserved traces of color upon their skin, we are certain that they were entombed before decomposition of their soft parts had taken place." In the so-called Devonian rocks of Ohio, hundreds of feet thick, from the top to the bottom are found the remains of sharks of all sizes, and the remains of these fishes when unearthed tell the following tale. They died in the natural swimming position, belly down, and the weight of the mud that settled upon them from above flattened them to the thickness of a quarter of an inch. Such things point to a catastrophe of the nature of the Flood.

In Sioux County, Nebraska, there is a hill called "Carnegie Hill" which has been formed by the erosion of the level Nebraska prairie by the Niobara River and its tributary streams. The hill was once an integral part of the entire Nebraska plateau and the horizontal layers in the hill are the same as in other, similar hills nearby and in the Nebraska plateau as much as fifty miles away. In that one hill, forty feet below the top, is a horizontal layer of the jumbled remains of nine thousand (estimated) animals not now native of America, embedded in the almost pure, white limestone of which the hill and the plateau is composed. The remains of other kinds of animals are entombed in the same sort of horizontal strata in the entire western part of Nebraska. (Fig. 26.)

Evolutionary geologists are not able to deny the numerous indications of the catastrophic, watery deaths and burials of immense numbers and quantities of plants and animals whose remains are found in the earth, but being determined to ignore the meaning and truth of what the Bible says about the Flood throughout its pages, they attribute these watery deaths and burials to a large number

[68] *Geology and Mineralogy,* volume 1, page 124, 5th ed., 1858.

Fig. 26. Remains of camels, pigs and rhinoceroses entombed in limestone at Agate Springs, Sioux County, Nebraska. The rock has been carefully removed from the bones. Evolutionists claim that these were buried when the animals fell into a sink-hole at a watering place, but the fact that they are entombed in pure limestone and are in a horizontal layer which extends for miles beneath the prairie belies that claim. (Photo by the American Museum of Natural History.)

of catastrophes which occurred at different times during hundreds of millions of years. There is, however, no need of this. One catastrophe, the Flood, when properly understood can account for all. It is not sensible to multiply causes when one will do. No thoughtful Flood-geologist will call the Deluge a simple affair nor deny that its geological work is not always easy to interpret, although he has good reason to insist that his task is always very simple compared with the magnitude of the task which faces the evolutionary geologist as he attempts to explain the countless difficult situations which confront him on the basis of his non-Flood or "uniformitarian" theory.[69] In the light of Scripture and nature the Flood is to be regarded as having continued, in its *geological effects,* for many thousands of years [70] after it had once begun—until a condition of earth-stability was reached. It can not be thought that the entire world's surface was uprooted by the Flood in the manner in which the Bible implies [71] and a geological situation not arise whereby great natural changes would continue to occur for a long time. Some fossils which would not at first be regarded as having been caused by the Flood, and which can not be directly attributed to it, can be indirectly attributed to it. The Deluge of the Bible can account for the fact that such deep-sea creatures as the star-fish, crinoids and corals are usually, though not always, found today in the deeper layers of earth. It can explain why the higher vertebrates, the land animals, supposed to have evolved last, are usually, but not always, found in the upper earth deposits.

---

[69] The immense quantities of oil in the earth are today analyzed by chemists as the altered remains of immense quantities of ancient animal life, particularly ancient sea-animal life. Oil is somewhat of the nature of coal. Nothing taking place in nature today can account for the presence of such great quantities of animal life deep in the entire earth's strata. The Flood, a distinctly supernatural and divinely ordered event, can account for it.

[70] Ussher's chronological system, which places the Flood about 2353 B.C., must be regarded as totally false both to the Bible itself and the evidence of nature. See the chapter on Biblical chronology in the author's *Before Abraham.*

[71] Genesis 6:13, "I will *destroy* them with the *earth*"; II Peter 3:6, "the *world* that then was, being overflowed with water, *perished.*"

As the believer in the Bible enters into any of the large museums of the land, such as the Museum of the Smithsonian Institute in Washington, D. C., where many thousands of fossils of plants and animals are exhibited, he should divest himself of all notions that one fossil is millions of years older or younger than any other merely because some evolutionist has so labeled them, and conceive of them all as having lived at one time and died together.

THE "PROOF" FROM THE GEOGRAPHICAL DISTRIBUTION OF PLANTS AND ANIMALS

Because this proof is so vague that many evolutionists do not use it the writer would be justified in ignoring it also and would do so except that a brief discussion of the present distribution of plants and animals over the earth's surface will show that the Scriptures offer a completely satisfactory explanation of this problem.

The evolutionary "proof" on the basis of the geographical distribution of plants and animals consists essentially in one thing, namely, that of setting up a dummy conception of special creation and then knocking it down. A ridiculous and unwarranted doctrine of creation is attributed to those who accept the Biblical account, and a vague conception of evolution is postulated. When the absurd doctrine of special creation is destroyed by ridicule, the dogma of evolution is left standing and is thus "proved." The argument is, therefore, a purely negative one and requires that the creation explanation of the distribution of plants and animals be defended.

Just what that conception of special creation is which is attributed by evolutionists to those who believe the Bible is best shown by a quotation from Charles Darwin, which is quoted with approval by one of the late evolutionary propagandists, Vernon Kellogg. Darwin, after describing the plants and animals of the Galapagos Islands, 500 miles off the west coast of South America, and after telling how similar they are to those on the nearby continents, says, "Why should this be so? Why should the species which are supposed to be created in the Galapagos Islands and nowhere else (note the 'nowhere else') bear so plainly the stamp of affinity to those created in America?

79

Facts such as these admit no sort of explanation on the ordinary view of special creation, whereas in the view here maintained (i.e., evolution) it is obvious that the Galapagos Islands would be more likely to receive colonists from America by flight, on and in logs, than on the creation basis."[72]

It is evident from the above quotation that Darwin and those who approve his words think that the creation doctrine demands that every living organism was created just as it is and where it is; that the plants and animals of the Galapagos Islands were created there; that those of Wisconsin were created there; that those of England and Africa were created there. Whether they were or not has nothing to do with the present distribution of plants and animals in the light of Revelation, for since the creation all the animals of the earth were once destroyed by a great catastrophe by water and the world replenished from the ark.

The evolutionists themselves assume certain "centers of distribution," the chief of these being central Asia. This has been so stated by Henry Fairfield Osborn of the American Museum of Natural History, and thither, therefore, that institution has of late years dispatched Roy Chapman Andrews in hopes of securing evidence on some of the hidden problems of the supposed evolution. One wonders if these men did not get their idea of Asia as a center from the Bible, for the ark is believed to have grounded in that area.

It might be well to consider in the light of the Scriptures how the replenishing of the earth after the Flood took place. Into the ark had been brought two of every "kind." From the sacred record it appears that it was not necessary for Noah to go out into the world and collect these pairs, but that they were sent to him, they came to him, impelled by the Power which made and controls all things. That the ark was not large enough to contain two of every bi-sexual species has often been charged. The charge, however, rests on ignorance both as to the vast carrying capacity of the ark as outlined in the Bible, and as to the

---

[72] Vernon Kellogg. *Evolution the Way of Man*, pages 86, 87. Notes in parentheses within quotations in this book are the author's.

number of species that there actually are. Some scientists, called the "lumpers," make the number of species few. Others, called the "splitters," make the number many. Until breeding tests have been carefully applied so that men can know which forms are varieties and which are distinct species no one will be able to do more than make a guess at the number of "kinds" there are. Dr. Howard Osgood in the *Sunday School Times* [73] discusses the question whether all species of animals, as they are now classified by naturalists, could have found accommodation in the ark. The highest estimate of the number of species of land mammalia is 290 above the size of the sheep, 757 from the sheep to the rats, and 1,359 of the rats, bats, and shrews. The average size is about that of the common cat. Allowing five square feet of the deck room as amply sufficient for a cat, two of each species of mammalia could find room on two-thirds of one deck of the ark, with its 33,750 square feet of surface. The representatives of 10,000 species of birds, 979 of reptiles, 1,252 of lizards, and 100,000 of insects could easily be placed on the remaining third of the deck, leaving the other two decks for storing food.

Leaving the ark, each species began to "mutate" and produce varieties differing in some respect from the original parents (See Appendix II). As this multiplication and variation continued the species spread out continually into new and distant places. The natural species *song-sparrow* varied into the twenty to thirty known varieties found on two continents. The museum of Princeton University contains a large map of the North American continent to which have been pinned many different varieties of stuffed song-sparrows with a legend saying that this variation in different localities shows the influence of evolution. Joseph Grinnel, writing in the *Report of the Smithsonian Institute* on the "Geography and Evolution in Pocket Gophers of California," states that there are thirty-three distinct races of pocket gophers in California, occupying regions to which they are adapted from the hot, moist lowlands to the cold, dry highlands. Such sort of evolution the Bible lover can well agree to, for it is

[73] Feb. 6, 1892.

81

what is to be expected on the Biblical basis. Some varieties have found one locality suitable to their tastes and remained there, others have found other localities suitable. Squirrels, rabbits, and other species also varied into the numerous different types in which they were given power in creation to appear, and under one condition or another, according to the possession of a warmer or a colder coat of fur, or a more protective coloring, or some other advantageous inherited characteristics, the species have spread throughout the world. White animals are today usually found in the wild state only in the north where their color against the snow protects them.

The large part of the present distribution of plants and animals has likely taken place outside the influence of man. The population of America with animals and birds from Asia likely took place when the two continents were connected in the region of Alaska. Man, however, has had a part in the distribution, and the readiness with which certain species of plants and animals have multiplied and thrived when they have reached the localities into which man has brought them shows that not all species have yet found the regions to which they are best adapted. No rabbits were in Australia when the English came there. When introduced for hunting purposes they multiplied so rapidly as almost to destroy the cattle industry. No blackberries were in New Zealand originally. Upon being placed there by man they grew so rank as to destroy thousands of acres of valuable land. Man is responsible for the introduction into America of the English sparrow, which now represents forty per cent of the bird life of the land. Man re-introduced the horse into America.

On the evolutionary basis it is difficult to see why, if all species arose by themselves in response to certain environments, they did not originate in the regions where they flourish so well when once introduced. On the evolutionary basis of plant and animal distribution, which is a very vague one and is nowhere stated clearly, there are some serious problems to be faced. For example, how does it happen that the bison pictured on the caves of Europe so closely resembles the bison of America if they have not both come from a common pair as the sacred record indicates? For every difficulty that the Biblical explanation of the distribution of plants and animals may have to face, the evolutionary explanation has one to match it.

The theory of creation does not require, as Darwin and his cohorts have supposed, that the plants and animals of the Galapagos Islands or of any other islands or continents were created there. They may have come over from some neighboring place "by flight, on or in logs" as well on the creation basis as on any other; and there may be slight differences between the varieties in two geographical localities as well on the creation basis as on the evolution basis.

SUMMARY

The "proof from classification" is merely the arranging of living forms in a graded system from the simple to the complex according to a supposed evolutionary course. This proof assumes what is to be proved.

The "proof from comparative anatomy" rests on an interpretation of the similarity of animal structures that is not necessary. The similarity may be accounted for on the basis of a common plan in the mind of the Creator.

The "proof from vestigial organs" rests on the false assumption that there are organs in animal and human bodies that are totally useless. Ignorance concerning the functions of the various organisms of the human body does not constitute a proof that they have no function. Ignorance furnishes no arguments. The early force of the "vestigial" argument rested on ignorance. The least benefit a body derives from the presence in it of a so-called vestigial organ renders that organ non-vestigial, and it is now known that the human body derives much good from every part that is in it.

The "proof from embryology" consists in making untrue statements of facts, and rests on unnecessary interpretations of actual facts.

The "proof from geology" rests on the unwarranted assumption that future search of the evolutionists will reveal the millions of fossil links now missing, and rests also on the arbitrary arrangement on paper, according to

83

an evolutionary order, of fossil-bearing strata that are not in that order in nature. The fossiliferous condition of the earth can be accounted for on the basis of the Deluge.

The "proof from the geographical distribution of plants and animals" consists in setting up a false doctrine of the present distribution of plants and animals according to the Bible, then knocking it down again by ridicule. The Biblical view of the distribution of plants and animals coincides well with conditions of distribution as they exist.

CHAPTER III

Wanted: A Greater Than Darwin

ON the basis of the foregoing "proofs" the evolutionist says that evolution is a fact. As to the satisfactory nature of those "proofs" the reader is asked to judge for himself.

While bearing in mind the questionableness of this fact of the past and present evolution of plants and animals, the reader is now invited to a consideration of the various attempts that have been made to explain how this supposed evolution has and does occur.

If, as is claimed, all present forms of plants and animals with their marvelous complexity of physical structure have developed out of a simple, primitive one-celled ancestor, something must have caused it. How a feather came to be, how a hand, how an eye, how a wing—these are things the creationist wants and has a right to know before he, as a sensible person, should be expected to give up his faith in the creation account of the first chapter of Genesis. What has caused the development which the evolutionist says has gone on? How did species arise? How did change and variation take place?

For over a hundred years evolutionists have been busy thinking up an answer to the above fair and very vital question. All the greatest minds among them have been bent to the task, for they have truthfully felt they could never expect evolution as a theory to satisfy thinking people better than the creation doctrine until a satisfactory answer to this question had been given. Merely to say it happened, but to be silent as to *how* it happened, that hands, eyes, wings, came into existence without a Creator, this in itself would be a confession of defeat.

In answer to this question several famous explanations have been given. For a time one or two of these explanations were considered satisfactory by many evolutionists. Later, however, they had to be abandoned and new explanations sought. Today, as the reader will see after the reasons are presented, no evolutionist has any explanation of the problem to offer which is able to satisfy even those eager to be satisfied. All any evolutionist can do at the present time is to sit back and hope that some one of his fellow evolutionists will soon think of something.

It is well worth while for the reader to know the attempts which have been made to explain how the continual evolutionary change that is supposed to have gone on has taken place. It will impress upon him the magnitude of the task which those who would establish the evolution theory in place of the doctrine of creation have before them, and will convince the creationist that he has the only possible explanation of the origin of the present world of plants and animals that clear thinking persons can accept.

THE ATTEMPTED EXPLANATION OF LAMARCK

The first attempt to explain the workings of the evolution process was made a hundred and fifty years ago by a French evolutionist named Lamarck. Observing the everyday fact that if a man uses his arm vigorously for a time, as a blacksmith does, the arm becomes larger, and if he does not use his arm, but sits physically idle in an office as does a clerk, his arm becomes smaller, Lamarck thought he had found a solution of the problem. He said,[74] "The remote ancestors of present day forms were always being induced by the conditions in which they lived to use certain parts of their bodies more than others. Those parts that were used became larger. Those parts not used became smaller. The effects of the use or disuse of these parts were passed on to the offspring. They were slightly different from their parents. In turn the offspring themselves were caused by conditions in their environment to use one part

[74] This and the following are not exact quotations. They are intended merely to give the idea of what he said.

more and another part less. The results in them of this use or disuse of parts were still further passed on. Thus changes in the offspring, imparted to them by the varied use or disuse of parts by the parents, were steadily accumulated through the centuries, and by their accumulation living forms were continually undergoing a process of transformation."

To make this explanation of a difficult problem clear, a few concrete examples had best be taken out of Lamarck's book. Taking the case of the giraffe with its long neck, Lamarck explains it in the following manner: "The remote ancestors of the giraffe had short necks [75] as does the horse or cow. Along came a drought and dried up all the vegetation on the ground. Leaves remained on the trees, however. For these leaves the short-necked ancestors reached and in doing so stretched their necks. Then they had offspring and the offspring showed in themselves the effects of their parents' stretching. The necks of the offspring were imperceptibly longer than their parents'. The offspring grew up. Along came another drought which dried up the grass on the ground but left the leaves on the trees. For these leaves the ancestors stretched their necks. When their young were born they showed the effects of their parents' stretching. Their necks were still longer. And so on. By the steady accumulation through thousands of years of the effects upon the neck of stretching for leaves the present long neck of the giraffe came into being."

Another of Lamarck's illustrations was that of the long legged birds which love to stand in the water, for example, the flamingo. "How did that bird get such long legs?" we ask. Thus answered Lamarck: "Its ancestors had short legs. By continual effort throughout thousands of years to walk into the water and get food out of it without wetting its feathers the ancestors' short legs became longer and longer until they became what they are today." Of course, it is also assumed, as the legs grew longer the neck was continually stretched so the bird could reach bottom with its mouth.

---

[75] How they got their short necks is not explained.

However ridiculous these explanations may seem to us, Lamarck must be admired for making the attempt, something that evolutionists today, though they talk loudly about the "fact" of evolution, do not seem inclined to do. Foolish as these explanations are, let us critically examine them in the light of facts and common sense.

We have a right to ask, "Why do not other animals besides giraffes have long necks, acquired in the same way? Did no other animals live in drought-ridden areas? Did they move out of drought-ridden areas to better pasture lands? If so, why did not the giraffe's ancestors move out also, which is what wild animals usually do in such cases? How did it happen that between droughts, when the feeding was good on the ground, the necks of the ancestors did not again begin to shrink? The giraffe today lives in the open plains and feeds upon grass. Why, if all was as simple as Lamarck supposed, has not the giraffe evolved back into a creature that can eat comfortably, without having to spread its legs?"

Concerning the flamingo the question arises, "If getting fish-dinners was so awkward for the dainty short-legged ancestors of that tall bird, how did it happen that they did not become tired of such disagreeable meals long before any appreciable length in their legs was arrived at? Or, if their craving for small fish could not be gotten rid of through evolution, why did the ancestors not become ducks, as other birds, according to the theory, must have done, and learn to swim?"

Creationists ought to thank Lamarck for calling attention to such definite problems as these, which are only a few of countless other difficulties. Supporters of the evolutionary theory do not like to face things of this sort directly. They prefer to talk in general terms. They are accustomed now to laugh at Lamarck's explanation, call his illustrations crude, and disclaim any responsibility for them. Nevertheless the long neck and long legs are there waiting to be explained satisfactorily on any other basis except creation, and the creationist should demand a satisfactory explanation before he believes in evolution.

Besides such difficulties as the above there is one other serious flaw in Lamarck's attempted explanation. In the discussion of his concrete cases nothing was said about his supposition that the stretching of the parent giraffe's neck would affect the offspring, making its neck slightly longer. In other words nothing was said about the assumption that changes of body in parents, however slight, are transmitted to their offspring—for example, that big muscles gained by a parent through exercise are passed on as bigger muscles to their children, or, that the neck-stretching of an ancestor giraffe would produce by inheritance a longer neck in its offspring. As a matter of fact these are false assumptions.

It is popularly believed that if a person were to have his nose pulled and fastened over to one side of his face throughout life, the child of that person would inherit a nose bent at least slightly to the same side. Actual observation, however, has never yet revealed any authentic proof of the inheritance of this or any other acquired character. Soldiers who have lost legs or arms in war do not have legless or armless children. Many cases of the inheritance of acquired characters have been reported, but careful investigation has always revealed an error somewhere. It was once reported, for example, that over in Rutenberg, Germany, a cat whose tail had been cut off had given birth to a litter of bobtailed young. Here was a definite example of the inheritance of a mutilation. But further investigation revealed that the father was a bobtailed Manx cat.

By actual observation we know that a blacksmith may by use get a big arm. But his son will have to develop his own muscle or he will not have it. Parents may learn ten languages, but their children will have to begin with the A B C or be ignorant.

If acquired characters were inherited there are many cases where the fact would have had an excellent chance to establish itself. It is well-known that the old Chinese bound the feet of their female children for many generations. Yet the feet of Chinese women, if permitted to grow, were perfectly normal. The Jews have been circumcizing their boys for 4,000 years with no effect discernible in the modern Jewish offspring. How acquired characters are not inherited is well illustrated in the fact that cutting the hair for many generations has not made barbershops a whit less necessary.

It was an evolutionist, Weismann, who was advocating Darwin's theory against Lamarck's, who gave the death-blow to Lamarck's explanation. Weismann appealed to his fellow evolutionists' common sense. He pointed out how for many generations the tails of certain breeds of sheep and the combs of fighting cocks have been cut off with no effect upon the tails and combs of the sheep and cocks which descended from them. He himself cut off the tails of mice for nineteen generations and then gave it up. The tails of the last were as long as the first.

Weismann, however, performed a greater service to true science and to the cause of the Bible than merely cutting off the tails of mice. Convinced by experiment that acquired characters are not inherited, he began a study of living organisms which resulted in an important and vital discovery. He learned that there are two kinds of cells that go to make up the mass of any individual (1) body cells, and (2) germ cells. He noticed further that very early in the development of the embryo, even as early as the eight- and sixteen-cell stages in some animals, when the creature is the size of a pin-head, the germ cells are set aside. Set aside, they never change. They retain all through life the original character of the egg-cell, and they go to make up the reproductive cells of the adult. Out of these germ cells come all future generations. Weismann observed, however, that the body cells, which go to make up the eyes, hands, feet, change their character. He also observed that the germ cells are totally independent of the body cells and are not affected by changes in the body. The cutting off of a finger has no effect whatever on the germ cells out of which the next generation comes. As a result of Weismann's work, men have learned that the direct line of descent from generation to generation is not a descent from adult to adult but from germ cell to germ cell. As the Bible indicates, life is in the "seed" and the seed does not change.

The physiological explanation by Weismann of the fact of the non-inheritance of acquired characters is today universally accepted. It explains why a crooked nose, or a shaved head, or a cut-off leg does not and cannot result in crooked-nosed and bald-headed and one-legged children. It shows why evolution could not have come about in the fashion Lamarck imagined.

Inheritance of acquired characters is absolutely vital to Lamarck's explanation of the how of evolution. In fact, Herbert Spencer, one of the most prominent exponents of evolution in the nineteenth century, said, "Either there has been inheritance of acquired characters, or there has been no evolution." [76] According to prominent evolutionists themselves, then, there has been no evolution, for, as Prof. Lock of Cambridge University said, "It is generally agreed among them that acquired characters are not inherited." [77] Speaking of the inheritance of acquired characters, Prof. Kellogg of Stanford University said it "unfortunately does not seem to happen." [78] Prof. Conklin of Princeton University went so far as to say that "The inheritance of acquired characters is inconceivable." [79]

Considerably before the present day Lamarck's courageous attempt to solve the problem began to be abandoned. Charles Darwin, who had an explanation of his own to offer, said, in the middle of the last century, "Heaven forfend me from Lamarck's nonsense," [80] and his coworker Wallace added, "The hypothesis of Lamarck has been repeatedly and easily refuted." [81] At present the abandonment of Lamarck's explanation is practically complete. Prof. Morgan of Columbia University wrote, "Today the theory has few followers among trained investigators, though it still has a popular vogue that is wide and vociferous." [82] Prof. Kellogg said "The plausible and fascinating explanation of Lamarck, based on the assumed inheritance by offspring of changes acquired by the parents during the development and lifetime is found to be insecurely based. Acquired characters, in the Lamarckian

---

[76] *The Contemporary Review,* March, 1893.

[77] *Variation, Heredity, and Evolution,* page 115.

[78] *Evolution the Way of Man,* page 97.

[79] *Heredity and Environment,* page 240.

[80] Quoted from Lock, *Variation, Heredity, and Evolution,* page 115.

[81] Ibid., page 115.

[82] *Critique of the Theory of Evolution,* page 25.

sense, are not inherited. Hence, new species do not come that way." [83]

THE ATTEMPTED EXPLANATION OF DARWIN

The second endeavor to supply the dire need of a satisfactory explanation of the non-miraculous origin of the vast hosts of living organisms from a single speck of protoplasm was made by Charles Darwin and offered to the world in the *Origin of Species*.

This famous but now abandoned explanation had as its basis in nature two facts: (1) the variations among living things and (2) the struggle for existence.

Darwin noticed that not all offspring of a given parent are alike. They vary, though it be but slightly, in size, shape, and color. If one should examine carefully each one of the thousands of fish that are spawned each year by a single set of parents, it would be found that no two are exactly alike in every respect. Darwin further noticed that there is going on continually among all living things, man included, a terrible struggle for existence. Among the millions of fish that are born each year in the streams and lakes of the world only a few, comparatively, ever reach maturity. In one way or another they are lost during the struggle. What is true in the fish world is true in every sphere of life.

On the basis of the above facts in nature Darwin offered the following theory as to the origin of species. "From the beginning of life upon the earth the struggle for existence has been going on. In the midst of that struggle, accidental variation has always been taking place. No two forms have ever been exactly alike. Some of the differences have been bad or a handicap in the warfare of nature. Others have been good or advantageous in that struggle. Consequently, there was always a tendency on the part of nature to destroy the bad variations and preserve the good. It was this continual selection on nature's part of different forms that brought about the changes which produced the present animal and plant life."

In order to see how natural selection was supposed to

---

[83] *World's Work,* March, 1926.

work in actual practice, an illustration may be taken. The giraffe will again suffice. The problem for the evolutionist to solve is, "How did the long neck of the giraffe come into being?" [84] Granting the existence of a neck to start with, this would be the Darwinian explanation: "The ancient ancestors of the giraffe were short-necked. A severe drought arose in the land where they lived. This brought on a struggle for existence. The vegetation on the ground dried up. Leaves only remained to be eaten and they were on the trees. To get them they had to be reached after. The giraffe's ancient ancestors reached after them. When the lower leaves were gone only the upper remained. But not all those ancestors were alike. Some had slightly longer necks, and those that had them lived, while the others died. The drought passed. Presently another came along. Again the vegetation died upon the ground and finally leaves remained only on the higher branches. These only the longest-necked ancestors could reach. They did, however, and lived, while their less fortunate brothers and sisters perished. Again and again the drought appeared, for how many centuries, no one knows. It all happened, however, so as to accomplish the result of producing a neck in the giraffe species as much as six feet long."

Charles Darwin threw stones at Lamarck, saying, "Heaven forfend me from Lamarck's nonsense." It is an old adage that those who live in glass houses should not do such things. Surely Darwin's speculation is as laughable as Lamarck's.

"Natural selection" or "the survival of the fittest" made a great stir among those eager to get away from the philosophy of existence embodied in the doctrine of special creation. So great was the stir that the terms "evolution" and "Darwinism" came to be used synonymously. The enthusiasm that was engendered by it, however, did not last, and gradually this speculation also began to be abandoned. Today it is not accepted as satisfactory by any evolutionist of prominence in the world.

---

[84] The reader will readily be able to call to mind organs far more difficult to account for than the giraffe's neck, e.g., the heart, lungs, eyes, etc

Opponents of Darwinism have enumerated many objections to this once widely accepted theory.[85] It will be critically examined here from two points of view, from either of which its untenableness will be seen:

(a) *Darwin's theory begs the question entirely.* It assumes that which is expected to be shown, namely, how new species, new parts and organs of plants and animals came into existence. Evolution means producing new things, not only new individuals, but eyes, wings, fingers, beaks. Darwin's theory, however, merely assumes that these things were *in existence* and the better of them selected for survival and the poorer for extinction. For example, if two apples are on a plate, a man can select one and eat it. In so doing he leaves the other apple. This selection, however, does not explain how either apple came to be in existence. They were there before the man started to eat. Similarly, two evolving creatures may have been in existence long ago, one having parts of the body which made it more fit to survive than the other. Nature selected the more fit to survive and the less fit to perish, as Darwin said. But we have not yet had explained to us by Darwin how those parts of the body came to be. This is what we want to know. The views of a few keen-thinking men on this destructive weakness in Darwin's theory may be noted. Prof. Lock of Cambridge University says, "Selection, whether natural or artificial, can have no power in creating anything new."[86] Hugo de Vries said, "Natural selection may explain the survival of the fittest, but it cannot explain the arrival of the fittest." [87] Alexander Graham Bell, the inventor of the telephone and a student of evolutionary problems, said, "Natural selection does not and cannot produce new species and varieties. On the contrary its sole function is to prevent evolution." [88] Prof. Coulter of the University of Chicago says, "The most fundamental objection to the theory of natural selection is

---

[85] For a full enumeration of the impossibilities of Darwinism the reader is directed to the book of C. C. Coe, *Nature versus Natural Selection.*

[86] *Variation and Heredity,* page 40.

[87] *Species and Varieties,* pages 825-6.

[88] *World's Work,* Dec. 1913, page 177.

that it cannot originate characters; it only selects among characters already existing." [89]

(b) *Darwin said, "Natural selection acts only by the preservation and accumulation of small inherited modifications."* [90] *"If it could be demonstrated that any complex organ existed which could not possibly have been formed by numerous, successive, slight modifications, my theory would absolutely break down."* [91] *On Darwin's own basis, therefore, if it is possible to call to mind any structure of any creature which could not be imagined to have come into existence slowly and gradually through thousands or millions of years by the accumulation of tiny changes, Darwin's theory would have to be abandoned by any unprejudiced person. Such structures are numerous,* and a brief list of them will now be presented. Among them are some that would need to have been possessed in perfection from the very start or the possessors of them would have perished. To have possessed them in a third or a half developed condition would have resulted in the complete extinction of the evolving individuals.

1. *The wings of bats and birds.* The theory of evolution supposes that all the creatures which fly, such as bats and birds, are the result of an evolution of animals that once ran upon the ground. Birds are said to be an evolution from the reptiles. Bats are said to be an evolution from some mammalian forms of the type of the mouse. The wings of bats and the wings of birds are said to be the results of the evolution of the front feet of ancient ground-running reptilian or mammalian creatures. The Darwinian explanation of how this came about is that front feet changed slowly and gradually into wings in both birds and bats, because each modification wing-ward was helping in the struggle for existence. It may well be asked, however, if the *contrary* was not the exact case. When the change was slowly taking place during the thousands of years that it must have taken, and the wings were only half made, how did the evolving creature manage to survive? As the toes of the bat were slowly lengthening,

[89] *Fundamentals of Plant Breeding*, page 34.
[90] *Origin of Species*, 5th ed., page 110.
[91] Ibid., page 277.

and a thin membrane was being stretched between them, and the process was a third, or a half, or two-thirds complete, at which stages the creatures had neither feet for running nor wings for flying, but were left to flounder about in a helpless fashion, can it be conceived that they were enabled to survive in the terrible struggle for ex-

Fig. 27. Imaginary course of evolution of the bat. The Darwinian theory of evolution is that the bat has evolved through a period of several millions of years by slow, imperceptible changes from the mouse or some other ground-running creature. It must, therefore, have passed through millions of intermediate stages. It is inconceivable that the evolving creatures could have lived while in any of the intermediate stages numbered 2, 3, 4, 5, 6, 7, 8, for the fore-limbs were then neither feet to run with, nor wings to fly with, but useless appendages which would have made it impossible for the possessors of them either to procure food or to escape from the thousands of enemies which surrounded them. The above applies with equal force to birds, whose wings, theoretically, evolved from the front feet of reptiles.

istence which Darwin accepted as a fact? The answer is negative. Rather would the entire species have perished long before the wings had become complete.[92] There is no

---

[92] It is noteworthy that no fossils of creatures representing this vast gradual change from four-footed animals to winged creatures are found anywhere in the fossiliferous deposits. The immense numbers of necessary intermediate forms are conspicuous for their absence.

satisfactory explanation of the origin of wings except that of special creation. Reason agrees that "God created— every winged fowl" and did so "after its kind." [93]

2. *The spinnerettes of spiders*. In the rear body-part of spiders is a group of specialized organs which the insect uses to make the gossamer web on which its very existence depends. The structure of the organs is truly marvelous. Inside the body are numerous cavities or glands which are full of liquid silk. The glands are like bulbs which can be pressed by the surrounding muscles and the liquid silk squeezed out. When expelled, the liquid passes out through hundreds of exceedingly tiny holes. Coming into contact with the air the liquid dries and threads microscopically thin are produced. These threads are then seized by several hundreds of spool-like organs and spun into a silk cord as fine and delicate or as thick and strong as is required. With the cord thus produced the spider makes his web and with it catches his prey. Of what conceivable value, however, could such a set of marvelous organs be in the struggle for existence in the initial stages of their development? Until they were complete enough to produce the delicate web they could only have been a dangerous nuisance to the possessor. On the basis of special creation, however, no difficulty is offered to a reasoning mind.

3. *Mammary glands*. There is a group of animals classed by students of biology as "mammals" because of the presence in them of mammary glands or breasts, by which the infant offspring in the early part of their young lives are fed with milk. Upon these glands the young of all mammals are utterly dependent for their existence. However, upon the Darwinian basis that these organs came into existence slowly through almost countless years by the accumulation of tiny changes in animal organisms, one may well wonder how the new born offspring managed to live during those times. If the delicate offspring lived on other food besides milk, which is difficult to imagine, what caused the mammary glands to develop? If the glands developed because the offspring sought for food in the region of the mother's breast, how did the offspring sur-

---

[93] Gen. 1:21

vive before food was to be had? Problems such as these are not answered by any theory of a survival of the fittest in a struggle for existence. They are answered by the theory of creation.

4. *Reproductive organs.* Living things are generally divided into two sexes, male and female. In both sexes, whether plants or animals, the reproductive structures are perfect complements of one another. It may be asked: How, on the basis of a gradual evolution, was reproduction able to take place while as yet these complementary sexual structures were a third or a half made? The egg-cells within the females of bi-sexual plants and animals have in them certain forms which call for similar forms in the sperm-cells of males of the same kind. Again it may be asked: How, on the basis of a slow evolution of these egg and sperm-cells was reproduction ever enabled to take place when the evolution was only a third or a half complete?

5. *Instinct.* It is the instinct of every newly born off-spring of mammalian parents to suck as soon as it is born. In no mammalian species is that instinct lacking. It need not, nor can it, be taught. The offspring sucks naturally, otherwise it would perish and the species cease to exist. On the basis of evolution by slow and gradual change it is impossible to see how mammalian species did exist, for with the sucking instinct only partially developed the offspring must promptly have perished. The instinct must have been put into those animals possessing them fully made by a Creator.

To all clear-thinking men and women there can be no satisfactory explanation of the origin of wings, reproductive organs, instincts, and a thousand other physical and psychical structures except that they were given to creatures fully made in the beginning.

Darwinism, once considered so satisfactory an explanation of the origin of all the physical structures which plants and animals possess, is no longer accepted by the vast majority of evolutionists. Besides those considerations presented here numerous others have led to its rejection. That it is rejected today is apparent from the following quotations by prominent evolutionists. "Darwin's explanation of organic evolution is now held to be an inadequate explanation." [94] "I have never been satisfied that Darwin's explanation is the rightful one." [95] "A new generation has grown up that knows not Darwin." [96] "He [Darwin] has been shorn of his selection theories as completely as Samson was shorn of his locks." [97] "Darwin speaks no more with philosophical authority." [98] "Similarly, the more widely accepted and apparently vigorously logical explanation of Darwin, based on the assumption of a life or death determining value of actually occurring many small variations in the struggle for existence, is also seen to be more logical than real." [99]

But though Darwinism, or natural selection, has had to be abandoned as a satisfactory explanation of evolution, it must not be denied that natural selection has played and does still play a large part in adjusting natural species already existing to the physical world. The earth has undergone marked changes since species were first created, and species have had to adapt themselves to new environments. In His wisdom the Creator made ample provision for species to adapt themselves to these changed conditions. He provided species with a great capacity to vary, and thus offered the material which nature might select and fit into these changed conditions, except where the changed environment required a power of variation greater than that with which the species were endowed. But, however much selecting nature may have done in the past, its selecting has never been able to originate anything. Natural selection can be only a mechanism for the elimination of what already exists.

[94] Prof. Coulter of the University of Chicago in *School Science Series,* page 16.

[95] Prof. Scott of the University of Princeton in *The Theory of Evolution,* page 25.

[96] Dr. Scott, President of the Botany Section of the British Association for the Advancement of Science, in *Nature,* Sept. 29, 1921.

[97] John Burroughs, famous naturalist, in the *Atlantic Monthly,* August, 1920.

[98] Prof. Bateson, President of the British Association for the Advancement of Science, in *Nature,* August 20, 1914.

[99] Vernon Kellogg in *World's Work,* March, 1926.

THE ATTEMPTED EXPLANATION OF DE VRIES

The last great speculation as to the cause of evolution was offered about the year 1900 by Hugo de Vries. According to the two previous attempts evolution was said to have come about very gradually, by little, infinitely minute additions, so slowly and gradually as to be unnoticeable. In the attempt to be considered now we have something entirely new and different.

De Vries was a botanist. While experimenting in his garden with a plant called Oenothera *(primrose)* he found that from it came forms such as he had never seen before. These he called "new species." They appeared unexpectedly among the offspring. As a result he offered the following explanation of how living things evolved. "New species," he said, "rose suddenly, spontaneously, by steps, by jumps. They jumped out among the offspring." His speculation was called, therefore, the "mutation" theory.

This theory, while it aroused great hopes among evolutionists for a few years, soon went the way of its fellows, when it was learned that the "new" species of plants which de Vries thought he had seen produced in his garden were discovered to be but one of the many varieties of forms which the Oenothera is privileged by the Creator to have. In an address at Toronto to the assembled scientists of America, Prof. William Bateson said, "Twenty years ago de Vries made what looked like a promising attempt to supply this (evidence of new species appearing among natural offspring) as far as Oenothera is concerned . . . but in application to that phenomenon the theory of mutation falls. We see novel forms appearing, but they are no new species of Oenothera. For that which comes out is *no new creation*." [100]

The abandonment of the speculation of de Vries as to the how of evolution was acknowledged by Prof. Jeffrey of Harvard University in the following words, "The mutation theory of de Vries may now be relegated to the limbo of discarded hypotheses." [101] (Appendix II.)

Today no evolutionist has anything to offer to account

[100] *Science,* Jan. 20, 1922.
[101] *Science,* April 3, 1914.

for the evolutionary process which is said to have taken place. "When students of other sciences," said Bateson, "ask us what is now currently believed about the origin of species, we have no clear answer to give. Faith has given place to agnosticism," and "That essential bit of the theory of evolution which is concerned with the origin of species remains utterly mysterious," and "We cannot here and now explain how species arose." [102] "Old explanations of evolution do not explain it," acknowledged Prof. Kellogg.[103] "These things are an illustration of the bankruptcy of the present theory of evolution," wrote Prof. Holmes of the University of California.[104]

One wonders how long the evolution theory is going to last without that essential bit of the theory which tells how and why such marvelous things as a butterfly, a trout, a robin, a lamb, a man were produced purely by forces of nature working naturally, such marvelous things as the Christian believes required supernatural power and wisdom, definite creative acts, for their production. The theory of evolution is at present lacking an explanation of how organs and species were produced. Unless someone comes soon to its rescue how long can the theory hold? Meanwhile, it is being held by evolutionists, in the words of Bateson, as an act of *faith,* while they wait for another greater than Lamarck, or Darwin, or de Vries. The difficulties to be faced in old problems and in new problems are so great that the final question will have to be not "how did it happen," but "did it ever happen at all."

SUMMARY

The theory of evolution should not be accepted in place of the doctrine of creation until evolutionists have answered the question, "How were forms produced by the operation of purely natural laws?"

Lamarck's explanation of how present forms evolved non-miraculously is not acceptable, and is not accepted by

---

[102] *Science,* Jan., 1922.
[103] *World's Work,* March, 1926
[104] *Science,* Sept. 3, 1915.

evolutionists today. The chief reason is that acquired characters are not inherited.

Darwin's explanation is not acceptable, and is not accepted today by evolutionists as a complete explanation because (1) selection can only take away. It cannot produce. (2) There are many organs of living things which would have been not only not a help to an evolving creature, but would have been a destructive hindrance in the great struggle for existence if possessed in an imperfect state.

De Vries' explanation is not acceptable, and is not accepted by evolutionists today because what de Vries thought were new species were found to be nothing but unknown varieties within old species.

Evolutionists today have no explanation of how living forms evolved.

CHAPTER IV

Mendelism: The Last Word on Evolution

AFTER ITS KIND, the first word on evolution, and forever decreeing its impossibility, was spoken by God at creation and given to men as a revelation through the Book. In the laws of Mendel, as they are called in honor of the man who first discovered them, we have what is entitled to be called the last word on evolution. The latest results of modern biological research, Mendel's Laws, agree exactly with what was written by Moses three thousand years ago—and they also elucidate it.[105]

Gregor Mendel was an Austrian monk who lived about the middle of the last century. He was a biologist of note. While experimenting with garden peas he made a discovery. He learned that peas do not vary in heredity in any such a slip-shod, haphazard fashion as was supposed by Darwin, Lamarck, and others, but according to definite, orderly laws which he recognized and formulated. Enthusiastic over his discovery, he wrote a paper on the subject and read it before the Natural History Society of Brunn, Austria, in 1866. At that time scientific men were all absorbed with Darwin's theory of evolution by slow, gradual, minute additions, and such information concerning the heredity of plants and animals as Mendel had discovered did not fit in well with Darwin's teachings. Mendel's discovery, therefore, was ignored completely, and it lay buried and unknown for thirty-five years. Not until the year 1900 was it brought to light when it was rediscovered independently by de Vries and Correns.

---

[105] Instead of speaking of the "laws of Mendel" or "Mendelism" biologists now speak of the "principles of genetics" to which Mendel's discovery led, but we have chosen to retain the original expressions, "laws of Mendel" and "Mendelism."

The principles and laws of heredity discovered by Mendel, when they became thoroughly known, completely changed the old ideas of scientists in regard to heredity. They revolutionized the notion of evolution which was popular in Darwin's day. Bateson, the famous British biologist and student of Mendelian heredity, said that

Fig. 28. Gregor Mendel. Mendel is an answer to those evolutionists who say theologians have no scientific ability and can know nothing about evolution.

Darwin would never have written the *Origin of Species* if he had known Mendel's work. Not only this, but Mendel's discoveries went far to destroy the faith of biologists in evolution itself. "It comes to pass that some biologists of the greatest authority in the study of Mendelian prin-

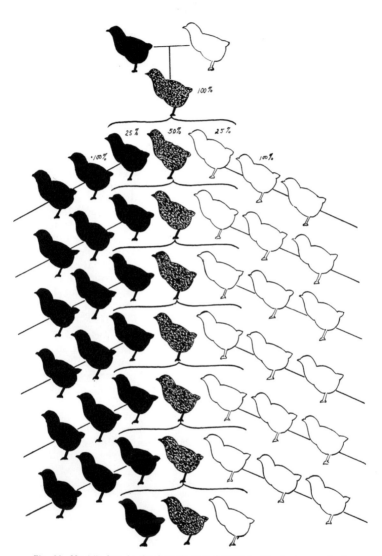

Fig. 29. Mendel's Law in the domestic fowl *Andalusian*. The dominance of color over non-color is incomplete.

ciples of heredity are led to the expression of ideas which would almost take us back to *creationism.*" [106] These words were spoken at Harvard University in 1916 by Prof. Caullery of the Chair of Evolution of the University of Paris.

From the beginning a pronounced dislike for Mendel's laws was apparent on the part of evolutionists. Alfred Russel Wallace, Darwin's close friend and co-worker, said, "On the general relation of Mendelism to evolution, I have come to a very definite conclusion. That is, that it is really antagonistic to evolution." [107] The evolutionist Caullery, quoted above, said, "The data of Mendelism embarrass us very considerably." [108] Professor Scott of Princeton, another evolutionist, has said, "Interesting and profoundly important as are the results of Mendelian investigation, it must be admitted that they have rendered but little assistance in making the evolution process more intelligent, but instead of removing difficulties have rather increased them." [109] Bateson revealed the situation when he said, "I notice that certain writers, who conceive themselves to be doing a service to Darwinism, take occasion to say that they expected as much (of Mendelism) and that from the first they *disliked the whole thing.*" [110]

The blow that the evolution idea has received from the discovery of Mendel's laws is well presented in the words of E. W. McBride, Prof. of Zoology in the Imperial College of Sciences, England. "I well remember the enthusiasm with which the Mendelian theory was received when it was first introduced to the scientific world in the early days of this century. We thought at last the key to evolution had been discovered. But as our knowledge of the facts grew, the difficulty of using Mendelian phenomena to explain evolution became apparent, and this

---

[106] *Smithsonian Institute Report,* 1916, page 343. The eminent Frenchman, Dr. Doumergue, in an article in *Foi et Vie* on the status of the theory of evolution in France, says that Prof. Caullery now (1925) "refuses to teach evolution, finding it of little interest."

[107] *Letters and Reminiscences,* page 340.

[108] *Smithsonian Institute Report,* 1916, page 333.

[109] *Theory of Evolution,* page 163.

[110] *Nature,* May 10, 1924.

early hope sickened and died. The way that Mendel cut was seen to lead into a cul-de-sac (blind alley)." [111]

So important is the bearing of Mendel's discovery upon the Biblical account of creation that an effort will now be made to give by illustration some indication of what Mendelism is. For complete information the reader is

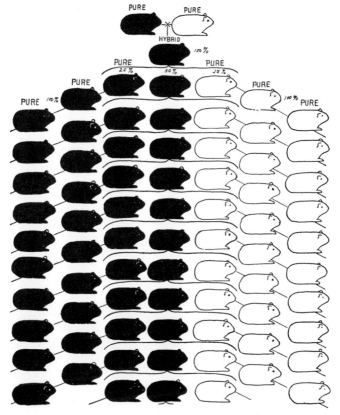

Fig. 30. Mendel's Law in hair colors of *Guinea-pigs*. The dominance of color over non-color is complete.

[111] *Science Progress*, Jan., 1925.

referred to one of the many books written especially on the subject.*

There is a common breed of chickens called the Andalusian. The breed occurs in three colors: black, white, and a mixture of black and white feathers called blue. (Fig. 29.) When a black Andalusian fowl is crossed with a white Andalusian all the chicks produced are blue.[112] The blue chicks, when they mature and are bred among themselves, do not produce all blue offspring. They produce three kinds of chicks in a definite, invariable proportion: twenty-five per cent black, fifty per cent blue, and twenty-five per cent white. The black chicks, when crossed together, produce black offspring. The white chicks produce white offspring. The blue, however, when crossed among themselves, produce the same definite proportion as before: twenty-five per cent black, twenty-five per cent white, and fifty per cent blue. This law of heredity has been revealing itself as long as the ancient stock of domestic fowls called the Andalusian has been used in poultry work.

There is a plant called the four-o'clock from its habit of blooming only in the late afternoon. (Fig. 31.) The flowers of this plant are deep red, pure white, and pink. Red, crossed with red, produces red. White, crossed with white, produces white. But red crossed with white produces pink. The whole generation of offspring produced by red and white mating are pink. When, however, pink is crossed with pink, pink flowers are not the only flowers that result. Red and white blossoms also appear, and always in the proportion of one red, two pink, one white. These second-generation red flowers produce red when mated with red; these second-generation white flowers produce white when mated with white; but the second-generation pink produce, when mated with pink, pink, red and white flowers, and always in the ratio of red 25: white 25: pink 50. This process is capable of continuing on indefinitely.

Still another illustration may be taken to illustrate the feature of Mendel's Law called *dominance*. In the cases

---

[112] This is the "Andalusian" desired by poultry fanciers. It is not a pure breed but a hybrid. It cannot be made to breed true.

*See Appendix III, Section 2, page 198

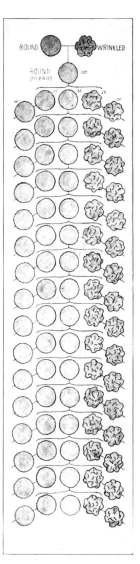

Fig. 31. Mendel's Law in the four-o'clock. Dominance of red incomplete.

Fig. 32. Mendel's Law in garden peas. Round dominates wrinkled completely.

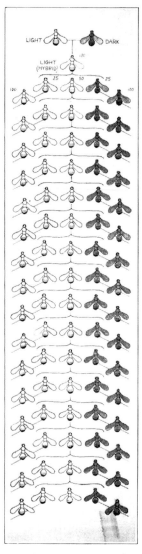

Fig. 33. Mendel's Law in the fruit-fly *Drosophila*. Light dominates dark completely.

Fig. 34. Mendel's Law in chickens combs. Rose dominates single completely.

thus far cited the hybrid, i.e., the product of the cross between two pure breeds, has been different from either parents.[113] The Andalusian, for example, which is produced by mating of a black fowl and a white one, is a black showing some white in the feathers. It is a black, but the dominance of the black over the white is not complete. The same may be said of the Four-o'clock. In most species, however, one factor dominates over another completely in the hybrid. Such is the case in the guinea-pig. (Fig. 30.) If a black or colored guinea-pig is mated with a white or uncolored guinea-pig, the first generation of offspring will be all black or colored. The factor for white is present in the hybrid but it does not appear. Here the color *dominates* over the lack of color, causing the hybrids to look exactly like the pure parent. They are, however, impure varieties, which produce, when mated with one another, one pure black, two impure blacks, and one pure white. The pure black will produce only black offspring. The pure white will produce only white offspring. The impure black will produce one pure black, two impure blacks, and one pure white.

From the above illustrations it is seen that species, e.g., the guinea-pig, contain certain "somethings" that travel down from offspring to offspring as units. The black color of hair and the white color of hair are the product of two distinct "somethings" which pass from generation to generation as if they were poured in at the top, and after appearing regularly along the way, come out at the end still intact. These "somethings" are called *genes*. Each natural species contains considerable numbers of these genes, which affect all parts of the organism and determine the color, size, shape which each part must assume. In dogs, for example, there are certain genes which have to do with the hair, making it long or short, rough or smooth, curly or straight, white or colored, plain or spotted as the

[113] Instead of "hybrid," the original designation after the discovery of Mendelism for the product of a cross between varieties, biologists now use the term "heterozygote," which means merely "impure breeding" or "mongrel." The word "hybrid" refers properly to such crosses between distinct species as mules.

111

case may be.[114] These genes are definite, fixed in number, and indestructible. They can combine in one generation in one way and produce a certain type of offspring. Then they can separate and combine again in another way in another generation and produce still another type of off-spring. (Fig. 35, 36, 37.) They can, however, produce no greater number of different types than there are genes that can be combined. What these genes are and how this separating and recombining of them again in each

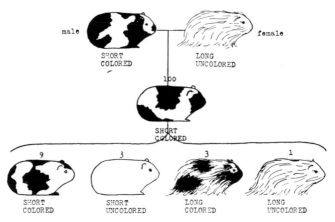

Fig. 35. The formation of new varieties within species according to Mendel's Law. As many different varieties can be formed as there are genes in the species which can be combined in different ways. In the above illustration a male and a female *guinea-pig* differ in respect to two pairs of contrasting character. The male has genes which produce short and colored hair. The female has genes which cause long and uncolored hair. Only the dominant genes show in the first generation of offspring, wherefore all are colored and short-haired. In the second generation four varieties appear. They are the result of various combinations of the four genes contained in the grandparents. Two of these four varieties are new in the sense that they are formed by new combinations of old genes. Nothing new in the evolutionary sense, however, has been added. The proportion of the varieties will be 9:3:3:1

---

[114] A brief sample list of alternating pairs of characters in different natural species is here given. In *peas:* tall vs. dwarf. In *wheat:* beardless head vs. bearded head. In *nettles:* much-serrated leaves vs. little-serrated leaves. In *cotton:* colored lint vs. white lint. In *carnations:* double flower vs. single flower. In *chickens:* feathered leg vs. clean leg. In *cats:* short vs. "Angora" hair. In *dogs:* harlequin spotted vs. plain color. In *cattle:* polled (hornless) vs. horned. In *horses:* trotting gait vs. pacing gait. The first in the pairs is the dominant.

Fig. 36. The formation of new varieties within species according to Mendel's Law when three pairs of alternating characters are involved. In the above illustration the male has the three dominant genes: shortness, color, and roughness of hair. The female has the three recessive genes: length, no-color, and smoothness of hair. All or a part of the dominant genes could as well be in the female and the recessive genes in the male. In any case the first generation of offspring would all reveal only the dominant characters. In the second generation eight different varieties appear, the result of that many combinations of the genes contained in the grand-parents. Still nothing new in the evolutionary sense is added. The proportion of the varieties will always be 27:9:9:3:3:1.

species takes place is now well understood and the descriptions of them constitute what are known as Mendel's Laws.

Certain general conclusions which bear upon the matter of the evolution or non-evolution of species in the light of Mendel's discoveries should be stated:

1. *Only those physical characteristics which are due to factors (genes) are inherited.* Variations in plants and animals are of two types: (1) those which are due to the influence of the environment, such as bleached hair or a tanned skin, and (2) those which are due to the existence of genes. The first types mentioned are not inherited. They are temporary, lasting only for the life of the individual, and are not passed on to the offspring. The second (genic) types are inherited, and are the only ones, therefore, of any importance in the matter of evolution. Darwin ignorantly recognized no distinction in the types of variations in living organisms in his argument for evolution.

2. *Wide and numerous inheritable variations are latent in natural species.* The Creator has given to living organisms, especially to the higher forms of life, a large number of the things called genes. The number He has given to the different species varies, but it is known that in most species, even in those of small importance in the eyes of men, there are known to be very many. In the tiny fruit-fly, Drosophila, for example, well over five hundred definite characteristics, known to be the productions of genes, have been discovered. The largest number of genes in any species, and consequently the greatest possibility of manifesting physical differences, is found, doubtless, in man.

3. *No visible variation outside the combination of existing genes can occur.* As a musician may combine the notes of his instrument in many different ways into the making of many different harmonies, so nature, by making different combinations of the factors existing in natural species, may produce many varieties in the species. Yet, just as the number of possible harmonies which the musician can make on his instrument is limited by the number of notes the instrument has, so the number of possible varieties which nature can produce in species is limited by the number of genes in them which can be combined.

114

By new combinations of old materials new forms may arise, many of them such as have never been in existence previously. A certain evolution, if one would care to call it so, takes place. Such evolution, however, occurs within a closed system, and does not destroy, but merely enlarges the Biblical concept of the creation of fixed types.

4. *No genuinely new, inheritable characteristic ever appears in species. Whatever appears was already contained in its ancestors in the form of hidden genes.*

In order for evolution to take place, new forms must come into existence. This is a *sine qua non* of evolution. These new forms must be new not in any relative sense, but in a real sense. They must be of the nature of new *creations.* Organs or organisms must come into existence which had no existence before. Since the rediscovery of Mendel's work attention has been fastened upon the apparently new forms which have been known to arise spontaneously in recent times in numerous species of plants and animals, e.g., sweet peas, poppies, wheat, corn, cattle, flies, moths and others. These "mutations," as they are called, have been said by evolutionists to be genuinely new creations, the materials with which the evolution process builds. De Vries, for example, considered the apparently new forms of the primrose, Oenothera, which appeared more or less regularly in his garden in Holland to be such new creations.

But mutations are not new things or new creations. Mutations are nothing but the revelation of the different effects of genes, or the revelation of the effects of different *states* of the same gene (some genes can have only one effect while other genes can have several and variable effects) which have been in existence in species as long as the species themselves have been in existence. As well call mutant forms "new" as call fish that appear periodically on the surface of the sea or of a lake "new" merely because they can not be seen at all times. For, variations in species which were thought to be new when they first appeared have later been seen to arise many times elsewhere, and variations which have been seen for awhile, and then have disappeared and seem to have become lost for good, have unexpectedly come back again.

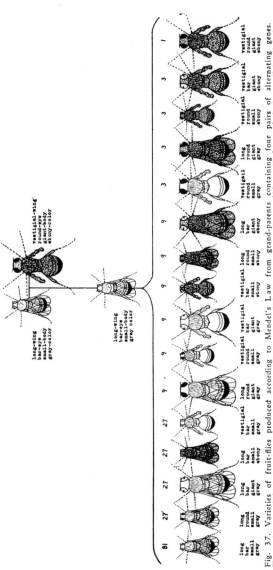

Fig. 37. Varieties of fruit-flies produced according to Mendel's Law from grand-parents containing four pairs of alternating genes. The pairs are (1) long wing vs. so-called "vestigial" wing. (2) bar-eye vs. round eye. (3) small (normal) body vs. "giant" body (body twice the normal size), (4) gray (sooty) color vs. black (ebony) color. The vestigial wing here pictured is capable of expanding when the air gets very warm.

116

There are now known to be many different types or causes of mutations and most of the types are fully understood—so much so that whereas evolutionists (like de Vries) were at one time greatly excited when they saw a strange form arising, because they thought they were seeing evolution going on, have now calmed down to almost complete silence. One of the simplest types of mutation is illustrated in Fig. 38. Other types are illustrated and explained in the appendix called MUTATION at the end of this book.

5. *The seat of all heredity is in the germ or "seed."* The conclusion which Weismann came to in his search for the reason acquired characters are not inherited, namely, that the basis of all heredity is in the germ, has been reached by students of Mendelism in an entirely different way. The seed of each kind is in itself, says the Bible, as if in the seed were to be contained the machinery upon which the eternal unchangeableness of species was to rest. All genes are passed on within the "seed," or germ, in what are called the chromosomes. Under powerful microscopes these genes can be seen inside the chromosomes, arranged somewhat like beads on a string (Fig 60.) An unconscious tribute to the statement in Genesis that the "seed is in itself" is found in the presidential address of Bateson as President of the British Association for the Advancement of Science, in which Mendelism was his theme, when he said, "Descent used to be described in terms of blood. Truer notions of genetic physiology are given by the Hebrew expression 'seed.' If we say he is 'of the seed of Abraham,' we feel something of the *permanence and indestructibility* of that germ which can be divided and scattered among the nations, but remains recognizable in type and characteristic after 4,000 years." [115]

GENERAL

Mendelian research has thrown remarkable light on certain problems at one time puzzling to the creationist. The "blind-fish" argument for evolution has been evaporated. Until recent times it was said by evolutionists

---

[115] *Nature,* August 20, 1914.

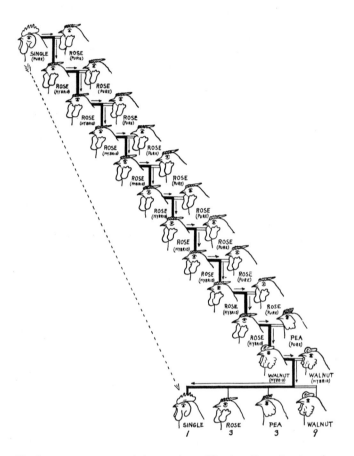

Fig. 38. Evolution means producing new forms. The above illustration shows how "new" forms may be nothing but old forms which, concealed for many generations, are revealed by an accidental mating. In actual practice a *single* combed fowl crossed with a rose combed fowl would produce *rose* combed chicks. The *single* combed characteristic has disappeared in the offspring. One of these *rose* combed offspring crossed with a pure *rose* combed bird would produce only *rose* combed fowl. After as many generations as the breeder might desire, during all of which the *single* combed feature would be hid, he could mate one of the *rose* combed offspring with a *pea* combed fowl. The products would be *walnut* combed. Two of these mated would produce offspring one of every sixteen of which would be a *single* combed bird.

that the blind fish of certain caves became blind because of the evolutionary influence of their environment. Their once perfect eyes evolved into sightlessness, it was said, because the creatures had been confined for so many countless generations in the darkness. Here, it seemed, the evolutionist had a definite example of the inheritance of an acquired character. While carrying on experimentation in search of knowledge of Mendelian principles, Prof. Morgan of Columbia discovered among the fruit-flies which he had produced in glass milk-bottles in the sunlight "blind" flies. (See Fig. 56.) They appeared in definite Mendelian proportions, they crossed back readily with parent forms, and could again and again be reproduced in the same fashion as at first, and thus demonstrated that they were merely one of the many varieties in which this species of fruit-fly can appear. Morgan therefore concluded, and all students of heredity have accepted his conclusion, that "eyeless" fish did not become eyeless because they had lived so long in caves, but that they were produced by their parents outside of caves and drifted or swam into them accidentally, and there, in a suitable, protected environment, continued to live. Morgan says, "Formerly we were taught that eyeless animals arose in caves. But they may arise in glass milk-bottles by a change in a single factor." [116] And Prof. Castle of Harvard, another prominent student of heredity, has said, "As regards the vision of cave animals, the Lamarckians hold that the eyes have degenerated because no longer used, whereas the selectionist holds that the animals which have taken to living in caves have been driven to this course."

Light has been thrown upon the whole problem of animal distribution and adaptation—or what may be called "a true evolution." After the Flood each species began to "mutate" and new forms began to arise. Among the cattle varieties were produced having short hair, such as is found in the Zebu of India or the Red Africander. Such a coat being better adapted to a hot climate, these varieties migrated to warm, equatorial regions. Other varieties were produced having long, warm coverings of hair, such as the

---

[116] *Critique of the Theory of Evolution,* page 67.

West Highlander and Galloway, or the prehistoric wild ox of northern Europe called the "auroch." These varieties migrated northward. Natural selection, working upon Mendelian or "genic" variations, produced all the evolution there is. Such evolution is strictly in accordance with what is taught in all Scripture.

An interesting side-light is cast by Mendelism upon the geographical distribution of mankind. The different shades and colors of the human skin, as well as all other features of his body, are now known to be due to factors that follow Mendel's Laws. The presence of the dark-skinned members of our race in the hot climates is not, therefore, to be explained on the evolutionary basis of inheritance of acquired characters, as due to the effects through many generations of burning sunlight upon the skin, but as due to the fact that after the Flood dark-skinned specimens of humanity drifted south into the lands of the burning sun, while light-skinned variations of humanity drifted north into climates more suitable for them. Africans are not dark because they came to Africa. They came to Africa because they were dark. "The darkest races of mankind are those which live where the sunlight is strongest and the skies clear; the fairest races live where the sun's rays are less intense and the skies are often overcast. This signifies to the Lamarckian that the effects of the sun's rays on the human skin are inherited; but to the selectionist it means only that men vary in depth of pigmentation and that each race has migrated to the climate which it is best fitted to endure." [117]

Knowledge of Mendelian laws of heredity was made use of to prove the non-inheritance of acquired characters. As was pointed out a few pages back, when two white guinea-pigs are crossed the offspring are all white, but when a white and a pure black are mated the progeny are all black, since black dominates white. Prof. Castle operated surgically upon a white guinea-pig so as to remove that part of the inner reproductive organs called the ovaries and put in their places the ovaries from a black guinea-pig.

---

[117] Castle, *Genetics and Eugenics,* page 40.—It is significant that "Ham," the name of one of the sons of Noah who was the progenitor of the negroes, means "black" or "dark."

When the white guinea-pig with the ovaries from the black animal was perfectly well, it was mated to another white guinea-pig. The question was: will the offspring be white, as from a cross of two white animals, or will they be black, as from a black and white? Will the eggs in the ovaries from the black animal be affected by their residence

in a white animal so as to cause a black offspring, if such is born, to be lighter colored? The offspring were all pure black, showing that the germ-plasm and the embryo in development were not affected by their environment. It is doubtful if any evidence can more clearly show the unchangeable nature of the germ or "seed," and how therefore species must bring forth "after their kind."

SUMMARY

Mendel's discovery has done great damage to the theory of evolution. Mendelism says: *After its kind.*

The chief facts bearing on evolution Mendel brought to light are (1) descent from generation to generation is orderly rather than disorderly, (2) variation takes place within natural species as a result of different combinations of materials already contained in the species, (3) nothing new is ever added.

Certain old, important evidences of evolution have been destroyed.

Light is cast on the nature of the pairs in the ark, and the repopulation of the earth with many varieties of animals from a comparatively few forms after the Flood is made clear and simple.

CHAPTER V

Bridging the Gap*

NO logical, consistent evolutionist will permit in his scheme of evolution any interference from an outside source. Evolution, according to him, is a natural process devoid of all that is supernatural and miraculous. To call in the help of the God-idea in order to get over difficult places in the evolutionary explanation of the present world, e.g., to account for the origin of matter, the origin of life, is declared to be "unscientific," and the policy rebuked as that of the "obscurantist," a term of derision or depreciation often applied to creationists. The supernatural cannot be admitted in one spot and logically excluded in another. The only consistent evolutionary position, and the only one worthy of intellectual respect is that of the evolutionist Huxley, who would not let God in anywhere, because, said he, "If you let God in one place you may as well let Him in all along the line."

It is, therefore, the statement of consistent evolutionists that man is entirely the product of evolution; that the regular, fixed, natural operations of matter which have produced the lower animals in their physical and psychic make-ups have also produced man, body and soul.

It is a lamentable policy on the part of creationists not to oppose the theory of evolution in the matter of plants and lower animals, but retreat before the attack until the evolution of man is reached and then turn and do battle. Such a policy is thoroughly inconsistent, since the same arguments which will prove the evolution of the lower plants and animals will also, if they are valid, prove the evolution

---

*The interested reader will find this chapter greatly supplemented in the author's book *Before Abraham* (Augsburg, 1948).

of man. One type of logic can not be accepted in one place but denied in another. Since, in the previous pages, the author has shown that the proofs and arguments for the evolution of the lower animals are not valid, he might well call a halt to this discussion. Nevertheless a few additional facts dealing particularly with the theory of human evolution may wisely be added.

THE EFFORT TO FILL IN THE PHYSICAL GAP BETWEEN MEN AND ANIMALS

Charles Darwin said that the evolutionary process produced two kinds of monkeys—the Old World apes, and the New World apes, and from the former man evolved. He especially designated the gorilla as man's most immediate ancestor among the brutes. In other words, according to Darwin, man came from a present-day monkey or ape form. Today, however, this is much denied. Osborn, head of the American Museum of Natural History and one of the leading American evolutionists, contended that man did not come from any ape, living or ancient, but that both men and apes branched off from a common spot on the evolutionary tree further down the stem.

The reason for this modern version of the theory, separating man from any living ape-form, is, partly, the fact that it is impossible to decide which of all the apes to select as man's ancestor.[118] The gorilla may be most like man in some respects, but it cannot be chosen as the ancestral form, because man's skull is smooth on top while the male gorilla's has a high bony crest in the shape of a chicken's comb. (Fig. 40.) Man has 12 pairs of ribs. The gorilla has 13. The gibbon cannot be chosen. It has a stomach most like man's stomach, also 12 pairs of ribs, but its arms, reaching down below the ankles, tell another story. The chimpanzee has short arms, but it has 13 pairs of ribs. The orang has a brain closest to man's for shape (highest in the forehead region) but the foot of the orang has a thumb instead of a big toe. All apes have this last feature in their anatomy, giving them the appearance of

---

[118] The following comparisons are found in Mivart's *Man and Apes.*

124

being equipped with four hands. The baboon's spine is most like man's spine, but in all other respects the baboon is widely isolated. The most human-like heads among the apes are found among some of the smallest, long-tailed South American monkeys. Mivart says, "It is manifest that man, the apes and half-apes, cannot be arranged in a single ascending series of which man is the culmina-

Fig. 40. A gorilla in its natural walking position. *Inset*, Gorilla skull.

tion." [119] "It should be borne in mind that it is to no one kind of ape that man has any special or exclusive affinity, and that the resemblance between him and lower forms is shared in not very unequal proportions by different species." [120]

Though man is not today said to be descended from

[119] *Man and Apes*, page 173.
[120] Ibid., page 193.

any living ape form, he is nevertheless said to be an evolution from some creature of the remote past which was ape-like in all its physical and mental characteristics. It may as well be called a monkey and the hair-splitting be done with.

On the basis of a slow evolutionary process from the amoeba to man there should be millions of connecting links all along the way. They should exist between apes and man. As Prof. W. B. Scott of Princeton says, "After all, what we want most is not *the* missing link, but *whole chains* which show clearly the descent of man." [121] This chain is admittedly lacking. While fossils of true apes, such as are alive today, are found, and many fossils of man, forms that represent states between them are not found. Evolutionists deny this, of course. They say fossils connecting men and apes have been discovered and they point to a large number of bones of considerable antiquity which they say proves their point. The most publicized of those will now be considered. It is impossible to speak of all the "proofs" of human evolution the evolutionists offer, since new missing-links keep popping up all the time. What is characteristic of the earliest and best known "proofs," now to be discussed, may be regarded as characteristic of all, even the very latest.

1. *Pithecanthropus Erectus,* the "Ape-Man of Java." (Fig. 41.) This so-called intermediate form is said to have lived approximately 500,000 [122] years ago and represented the first step of the brute in man's direction.

The following account is based on an article in the *Smithsonian Institute Report* for 1913. [123] In September 1891, a man named Dubois, while digging for fossils in the bank of a river in Java, discovered a molar tooth. The following month he found the top part of a skull about three feet away from the place where, a month before, he found the above mentioned tooth. A year later, in August, 1892, he found a thigh bone about fifty feet from the spot where he found the tooth and skull top.

---

[121] *New York Times,* Dec. 27, 1925.

[122] One "authority" says a million years, another something else. These and all similar estimates mean nothing.

[123] *Ancient Remains of Man,* by Dr. Alex Hrdlicka, page 495.

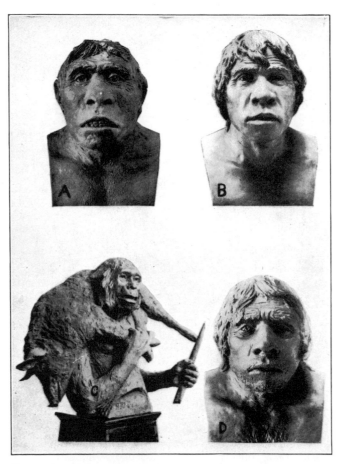

Fig. 41. Models of so-called "missing-links," based on bone fragments which have been found: (A) the Ape-Man of Java (B) the Piltdown Man (C) the Heidelberg Man (D) the Neanderthal Man. It should be clearly understood that these clay models are purely imaginary. They were moulded by Prof. J. H. McGregor under the direction of Prof. H. F. Osborn. *(Courtesy American Museum of Natural History.)*

In the following month, October, 1892, he found another molar tooth. These four bones, found in a region where the remains of many animal species were abundant, are the basis of the so-called ape-man of Java. (Fig. 42.)

Three years later Dubois brought the bones to Europe and laid them before the Third International Congress of Zoologists at Leiden, Germany. After he had made his report, Dr. Rudolph Virchow, the foremost anatomist of his day, criticized Dubois' report with the remark that, found as they were so far apart, there was no certainty that the bones all belonged to the same creature. Other scientists gathered at the convention examined the bones and could come to no agreement about them.[124]

Immediately thereafter Dubois carried the bones to his home in Holland and locked them in a closet, where they were kept, concealed from the gaze of men, for years. Thus spoke Dr. Alex Hrdlicka, in 1913, about this closeting of this "evidence" of man's evolution. [124a] "It would surely seem proper and desirable that specimens of such value to science should be freely accessible to well qualified investigators and that accurate casts be made available to scientific institutions, particularly after 20 years have elapsed since the discovery of the original. Regrettably, however, all that has thus far been furnished to the scientific world is a cast of the skull-cap, the commercial replicas of which yield measurements different from those reported taken of the original, and several not thoroughly satisfactory illustrations; no reproductions can be had of the femur or the teeth, and not only the study but even a view of the originals are denied to scientific men." If, as Dubois claimed, these bones were truly authentic evidence of man's evolution, it was indeed strange that they were kept in the darkness rather than in the light. Prof. W. H. Ballou, another evolutionist, in the *North American Review* of April, 1922, openly questioned Dubois' honesty in the

---

[124] To learn how widely the evolutionists differ in their interpretations regarding this and the other "missing-links" mentioned in these pages, the reader is referred to an article, "Controversy Over Missing Links" by G. S. Miller in *Smithsonian Institute Report*, 1928, pages 413-465.

[124a] *Smithsonian Institute Report*, 1913, page 497.

matter on account of his refusal to place the evidence where all men can see it. He said, " All we know about Pithecanthropus is what Dubois, the finder of the remains, gave out; who then sealed up the fossil and has hidden it for thirty years. We do not even know whether he told the truth about the remains or not, and are doubtful because

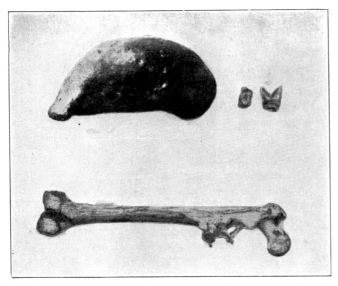

Fig. 42. Fragments of the missing-link "Pithecanthropus." They consist of a skull-cap, a femur, and two teeth. The skull-cap and the femur were found 50 feet apart. The teeth were found several yards from the skull. There is no certainty that any of the bones belonged to the same creature. Yet with these fragments as a basis, a creature of clay, half ape, half man in appearance, is constructed and offered to the unsuspecting public as a sure evidence of man's evolution from the brute. Note the high forehead compared to that of Lafayette in Fig. 48. (Collected from *Smithsonian Institute Report*, 1913.)

of his refusals to let anatomists have an opportunity to verify or disprove him."

Then at last, in 1923, under the pressure of scientific opinion, Dubois handed over his finds for critical examination. By this time he had carefully cleaned out the inside of the skull and made plaster-casts of its interior. It had been filled with solid earth when it was shown the only time at Leyden in 1895. Hrdlicka, then head ot the Smithsonian Institute, after examining the skull said that t "revealed a remarkable brain of unexpectedly human like confirmation." [125] The femur, Hrdlicka also said, was human, publishing an exact comparison of it with the femur of a person who had died recently.[126] Thus what had for many years been brazenly used by evolutionists as a proof of man's evolution was found to be not a proof at all. Dubois had gone to Java as a young doctor embued with the theory of evolution. He told his friends that he was going to bring back with him the missing-link. [126a]

2. *Eoanthropus Dawsoni,* the "Dawn-Man-of-Dawson." (Fig. 41B.) The second discovered form that is said to fill the gap between man and the brute is the so-called Pilt-down Man, named after the man, Dawson, who had the doubtful honor of having found it.

The manner of the discovery is worth relating in detail for the purpose of showing the amount of certainty or uncertainty, as the case may be, connected with this further "proof" of man's evolution from the ape.

Sometime about the year 1908 Dawson got from work-men digging in a shallow gravel pit at Piltdown, England, who had been requested to watch for fossils, a small fragment of a skull of some kind. Some years later (this is as Dawson reported it himself),[127] while visiting the same spot, Dawson picked up two more small parts of a skull, making three parts in all. Another year later, making the discovery extend through a period of three years by this time, half, or less than half of a jaw-bone of some man or animal was discovered. Dawson says that, guiding him-self by a tree close by, he concluded that the jaw-bone was found in the same spot as the skull fragments already mentioned. On the same occasion Dawson's friend, Wood-ward, found another tiny fragment of a skull. The year following the discovery of the half-jaw a priest named Teilhard found a tooth. In the same gravel were also found

---

[125] *Skeletal Remains of Early Man,* 1930, page 45.

[126] Ibid., page 62.

[126a] See the statements of Sir Arthur Keith in his *Antiquity of Man* regarding Dubois' early enthusiastic attitude.

[127] *Smithsonian Institute Report,* 1913, page 502

bones of the elephant, hippopotamus, beaver, horse, and deer. All the bones thus discovered, when collected together, constitute the remains of the Piltdown Man and are said to be evidence of man's evolution from the apes. (Fig. 43.)

Dawson and Woodward, before the discovery was quite complete (the single tooth not having yet been found),

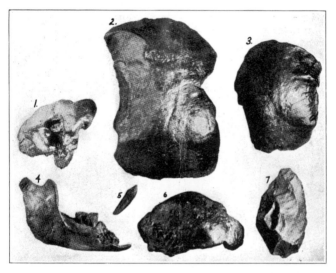

Fig. 43. Bone fragments which are the basis of the *Piltdown Man*: 1, 2, 3, 6, skull fragments; 4, jaw fragment; 5, tooth; 7, flint. *(The Hall of the Age of Man Guide Leaflet No. 52, American Museum of Natural History.)*

made a reconstruction with plaster of Paris of the skull of the missing link as they conceived it to be. (Fig. 45.) Motivated by the hope that they had in their possession a transition form between men and apes, they made a plaster model of a head—half man, half ape—giving to the head the size they thought such an intermediate creature should have had, that is about 1070 cubic centimeters brain capacity. Into this plaster head-cast they pressed the skull fragments as they supposed them to be related to one another. Into the jaw, which had been moulded into what was considered the proper chinless shape, they forced the half-jaw that had been found. They later gave the tooth a place next to the lower jaw.

However, all was not well. Sir Arthur Keith, the head of the English Royal College of Surgeons, himself an evolutionist, took issue with Dawson and Woodward as to the manner in which their reconstruction of the skull with much plaster of Paris had been accomplished. Keith figured the skull should be larger than they had made it. About 1500 cubic centimeters brain capacity instead of

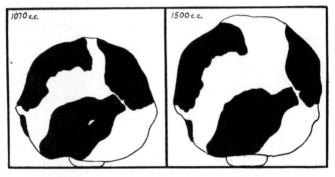

Fig. 44. Rear views of two reconstructions of the "Piltdown Man." The dark parts are the recovered bones. In fitting the bone-fragments together a storm of controversy raged between Dr. Smith Woodward, joint finder of the bones, and Sir Arthur Keith, both evolutionists. Woodward said the fragments should be arranged as seen at the left and that the brain capacity, therefore, was 1070 c. c. Keith said the fragments should be fitted together as seen at the right and the brain capacity was, therefore, 1500 c. c. These two rear views are copied from drawings by Keith and Woodward themselves appearing in *Nature* for Oct. 16, 1913.

1070 was his idea. Thereupon began an argument between the two, Keith on the one hand and Woodward on the other, which was carried on for months in the magazine *Nature,* as to the proper size of the skull. The fragments were arranged and re-arranged according to the whims of the contestants. No final agreement was reached.

In 1925 Keith wrote a new book on human evolution [128] in which he returned to the matter of the size of the Pilt-

[128] *The Antiquity of Man.* Lippincott, London, 1925.

down reconstruction and published elaborate diagrams and gave extended reasons why the reconstruction should be even bigger than he had contended for back in 1913, and declared, "Except for the thickness of the skull bones, the head is shaped and balanced as in us. In its general confirmation it does not differ materially from human skulls of modern type." [129]

Nor was all well among evolutionists with the single tooth and the jaw. By Woodward and Smith the tooth found by Father Teilhard the fourth year was assigned to the lower jaw of the right side. However, when the "evi-

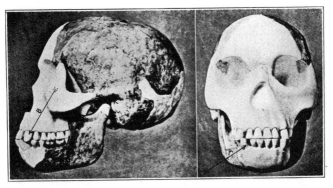

Fig. 45. Front and side views of the restored head of the "Piltdown Man." This restoration was made by Dawson and Woodward. It does not show the tooth because the tooth had not been found before the restoration was made. When the tooth was found Dawson and Woodward assigned it to the lower jaw of the right side where arrow A points. By other "authorities" the tooth is assigned to the upper left jaw where arrow B points. The white parts seen in the above view are made of plaster of Paris. The dark parts are the recovered bones. The right side (hidden from view) has only the smallest fragment of bone. The remains are bulked together on the left side. *(Smithsonian Institute Report, 1913.)*

dence" reached America, the tooth was assigned to a place in the upper left jaw by Osborn, Miller, Anderson and others. In America, therefore, this tooth resides in the plaster of Paris models in the upper left jaw. In Europe it resides today in the lower right jaw. The worst, however, happened to the half-jaw discovered the third year. It was emphatically declared by scientists of the highest stand-

---

[129] *The Antiquity of Man,* page 565.

ing [130] not to belong with the skull fragments at all and to be that of a chimpanzee.[130a]

A quotation from a well-known scientist will suffice to show the utter lack of scientific knowledge in the claims of evolutionists that in the Piltdown bone fragments there is a discovery of a genuine missing link. Prof. MacCurdy of Yale says,[131] "All the cranial (head) fragments, including the nasal bones, are human and belong evidently to one individual. They are, however, so incomplete as to leave room for a difference of opinion especially in regard to the capacity of the brain case. From the start there were not lacking those who hesitated to accept the cranium and mandible (jaw) as belonging to the same individual."

3. *Homo Heidelbergensis,* the "Man of Heidelberg." (Fig. 41C.) This man is said to have lived some 250,000 years ago. Publications dispensed by the American Museum of Natural History reveal this ancient mythical worthy with a slain boar thrown upon his back. Here, at last, the truth seeker expects to find a considerable amount of real evidence as a basis of it all. What, however, does he find? Merely a jaw-bone discovered in 1907 by two workmen in a sand-pit near Mauer, Germany. (Fig. 46.) The jaw-bone is uncommon on account of its rounding chin, but its shape can be duplicated among living human beings. (Fig. 47.) Its counter-part occurs quite often among Negroes. Its teeth are distinctively human. The well-known evolutionary anthropologist, Hrdlicka, says, "The teeth of the Mauer (i.e., Heidelberg) jaw are perfectly preserved and . . . they are unquestionably human teeth. They force the conclusion that their possessor . . . had already stepped over the line above which the being would be termed human." [132]

4. *Homo Neanderthalensis,* the "Neanderthal Man." (Fig. 41D.) The remains of this human being were dis-

---

[130] Sir Ray Lankester, Prof. of Zoology and Anatomy, University of London; Prof. Marcellin Boule, of the French Museum of Natural History; Prof. G. G. MacCurdy of Yale University; Prof. David Waterston, Prof. of Anatomy, University of London.

[130a] But see the human-like reconstruction shown in the author's *Before Abraham.*

[131] *Science,* Feb. 18, 1916.

[132] *Smithsonian Institute Report,* 1913, page 551.

covered in 1856 in a cave in western Germany by two laborers. They were carelessly dug up by the workmen so that many parts were lost. Only the skull (Fig. 48) and several parts of the skeleton were saved. At once a division arose in regard to the skull—some observers regarding it as modern-human and some (the more rabid evolutionists)

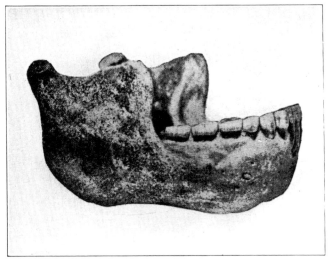

Fig. 46. The Heidelburg Jaw. Judging from its size it belonged to a man of the stature of Goliath. *(Smithsonian Institute Report,* 1913.)

regarding it as belonging to an unknown and primitive type of early man. The author has discussed the matter fully in his book *Before Abraham,* to which the interested reader is referred. Here it may be said that there are thousands of men living with skulls just as ape-like in every respect as the Neanderthal skull, which has a brain capacity of about 1330 cubic centimeters—that of the average male European.

Since 1856, when the bones of the first "Neanderthal man" were discovered, a very large number of remains of other men have been unearthed in caves and ancient burial grounds of Europe, Asia, and Africa. Out of these have been selected for evolutionary propaganda purposes the remains of several, those especially that have low human characteristics. These have been described in great detail and put in museums for exhibition. Among the most important are the Men of Spy, the Man of Krapina, the Man of Jersey, the La Chapelle-aux-Saints Man, the LaGuina Man, the Mousterian Man, the Peking Man, and

Fig. 47. Profile view of Marquis de Pinedo, famous Italian aviator. Observe that the same rounding, receding shape of chin is found in this brilliant man as is found in the Heidelberg Jaw. According to evolutionary methods Pinedo's jaw, if found in some ancient deposit, would furnish good proof of evolution.
(Wide World Photo)

the Rhodesian Man. They are all classed together as the Neanderthal race.

However, these men are all distinctly human. (See Fig. 48-50.) In brain capacity some far exceed the average American. The capacity of the La Chapelle-aux-Saints skull, for example, is estimated at 1,600 c.c. These men buried their dead. They used flint implements as did the American Indian of recent times. Some of the remains of this Neanderthal race show the effects of fire and wounds. The conclusion concerning it is, therefore, well summed

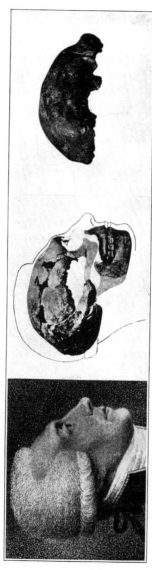

Fig. 48. *Left*—Marquis de Lafayette, Revolutionary War hero. *Center*—Skull of the Man of Spy No. 1, a member of the supposed missing-link race the Neanderthals, with profile of Lafayette superimposed. This skull might have belonged to Lafayette. *Right*—The original Neanderthal skull. (Drawing of Lafayette from Library of Congress. Skulls from *Smithsonian Institute Report,* 1913.)

up by the evolutionist, Sir Arthur Keith [133] who said, "In size of brain Neanderthal was not a low form. His skill as a flint artisan shows that his abilities were not those of a low order. He had fire at his command. He buried his dead. He had a distinct and highly evolved form of culture. Neanderthal was certainly not a dawn form of humanity."

5. The *Cro-Magnon Man.* Only briefly need this man be mentioned. He is distinctly human. Concerning him Osborn has said,[134] "The Cro-Magnons were people like

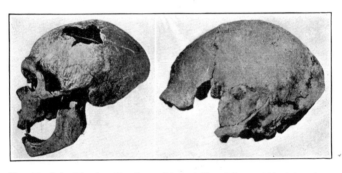

Fig. 49. *Left.* The La Chapelle-aux-Saints skull and jaw, which belonged to one of the so-called Neanderthal race. His brain capacity was 1600-1620 c. c., which is greater than that of the average European of today. All doubts as to his true humanity are removed by the fact that his remains were carefully buried in a rectangular grave in a cave in southern France. "Very plainly a regular burial," says Hrdlicka. *Right.* Skull of the Man of Spy No. 2, found buried with Man of Spy No. 1 (See Fig. 48). These skulls show that men varied in olden days as they do today. *(Smithsonian Institute Report, 1913.)*

ourselves in point of evolution, and the characters of the head and cranium reflect their moral and spiritual potentiality. This was a race of warriors, of hunters, of painters and sculptors by far superior to any of their predecessors."

The method adopted by those who are attempting to fill in the gap between man and brute from the evidence of human fossil remains should be clearly understood. Human beings vary in appearance because of racial pecu-

[133] *Antiquity of Man,* page 159.
[134] Revised 1923 *Guide Leaflet,* No. 52. American Museum of Natural History.

liarities, customs, diseases. Sex and age, not readily determined in fossil remains, determine to a great extent the size of the skull. Certain uncivilized tribes have had a custom of flattening the head of the child in its early years. Imbecility is a cause of abnormally large, abnormally small, or otherwise abnormally shaped skulls. The heads of pigmies, true men, are much smaller than the average human skull, being about 900 c.c. Some men have high foreheads. Some men have low and slanting foreheads. Yet the latter

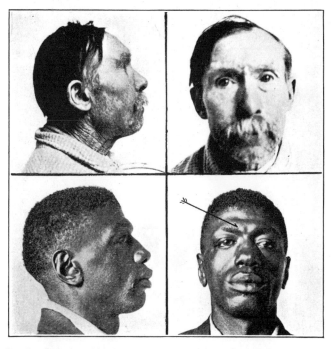

Fig. 50. Front and side views of two human beings whose skulls would make good proofs of human evolution if they were found in some ancient burial ground. Observe the low, slanting brow of the white man at the top, and the Neanderthal character of forehead—heavy supra-orbital arch—of the negro at the bottom (see arrow). A big supra-orbital bone merely means that there is a large sinus within. It is these types of human skulls which, when discovered by evolutionists, are used for propaganda purposes, while remains of equal age, but having more noble brows, are "placed to one side" and forgotten. Even better examples of this sort can be found among intelligent Americans.

may have as great intelligence as the former.[135] If, therefore, a man were seeking, as some are, for evidences of the evolution of man from the ape, it would not be difficult for him to find it among acknowledged human remains, by searching among the graveyards of men, rejecting those skulls with high, intelligent-looking foreheads, selecting those shaped so as to serve their purpose, and assigning to them the respective remote ages which their degree of

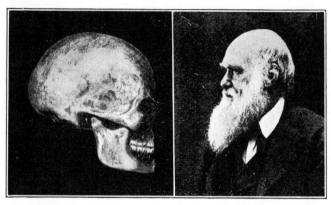

Fig. 51. *Left*—Skull of the Cro-Magnon Man, after the restoration by Prof. Rutot of Brussels. *Right*—Profile of Charles Darwin. The importance of this comparison is to show that 30,000 years ago, which is when the evolutionists say the Cro-Magnons entered Europe and drove out the Neanderthals, men were living with higher foreheads than those possessed by many brilliant men of modern times (see Lafayette, Fig. 49), higher and nobler even than that of the "intellectual giant," Charles Darwin.

ape-likeness permits. This is the actual method adopted by evolutionists. Out of the graveyards of Europe, when men of Europe were in a state of barbarism similar to that of our American Indian a hundred and fifty years ago, have been unearthed a very considerable number of human remains. Those mentioned in works of evolutionists, such as Osborn's *Men of the Old Stone Age,* or Hrdlicka's

[135] The evolutionist, Hrdlicka, himself a man with a low forehead, insisted that concrete evidence showed that height of forehead is no index to intelligence—men with low brows having just as high I.Q. on the average as those with high foreheads. See *Smithsonian Institute Report,* 1933, pages 406-07.

Skeletal Remains of Early Man, are only a few, carefully selected, of the whole number of remains discovered, remains which, as far as there is any evidence to the contrary, all belonged to men of the same age, i.e., the glacial period. These ancient remains are not all alike. They differ from one another as human skeletons differ today. Referring to the period when the Neanderthal man lived, Hrdlicka speaks of the "great variability in the skeletal remains of

Fig. 52. Chinook (Flat-head) Indians, after Catlin. The practice of flattening the human skull is of high antiquity. Low foreheads in ancient human remains may have been caused by artificial means or disease.

this time." [136] Those ancient human remains, therefore, that more closely fulfill the requirements of a link between man and his supposed ape-ancestors have been taken, measured, reconstructed, replicaed, and placed in glass cases for exhibition. Those that have not fulfilled the requirements have been "temporarily placed to one side."

That this is in fact the actual "scientific" method by which the gap between man and the brute has been narrowed is evident from the following words of Osborn,

[136] *New York Times,* Nov. 9, 1927.

141

"*Many finds* which have failed to satisfy the demands of science (i. e., evolutionary science) on one or more of the points of geological position, associated animal re-mains, associated implements of human manufacture, and morphological form (i. e., shape) have been *temporarily placed to one side,* to await the possibility of future discoveries throwing some light on their position." [137] The same laying aside of unfavorable human remains of the same age with those selected is also apparent from the statement of Hrdlicka,[138] *"In addition* to the more important skeletal remains of early man dealt with in the preceding pages, there exist *a considerable number* of specimens which, because of their isolated or defective nature, are of less value (for evolutionary purposes) to science, or which have not as yet been properly studied and determined, or which, finally, retain some elements of uncertainty as to their true position in human chronology. And *besides* these there is a large *additional series* of skeletal remains . . . which, while ancient, are nevertheless relatively near to man of the present date."

There is no sure way by which certain of those ancient human bones can be assigned to men who were "relatively near to man of the present date," while other ancient bones are assigned to men who were relatively far from man of the present date, except within very narrow limits. There is nothing in the places where the remains are found to make this possible. Few ancient burial places bear unmistakable marks of being either older or younger than others. There is nothing in the condition of the bones themselves. The fact that some bones are mineralized more than others is no criterion, for human bones buried in moist places are known to become heavily mineralized in a very few years. The flints and stone implements accompanying some human remains offer no basis of determination, for while George Washington was using silver knives and forks for eating, and using fire-arms in war in one part of the American continent, there were

---

[137] Taken by Prof. George McCready Price from a card in a show-case in the American Museum of Natural History, 1922. See *New Geology,* by Price, page 704.

[138] *Smithsonian Institute Report,* 1913, page 548.

Indians, true men, who were using flints and axes of stone in another part. In Zululand, in Africa, there exist today, overgrown with vines and underbrush, the ruins of once magnificent stone buildings, where now the natives live in grass houses and use spears and bows for weapons. At the present time, while half the world lives on a high plane of civilization, there are men who are living in the "stone age." There is small basis for saying, as the evo-

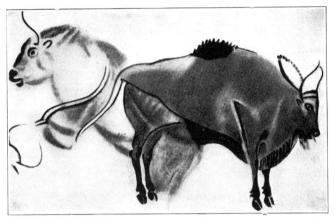

Fig. 53. Art work done by men properly estimated by evolutionists to have lived 20-25,000 years ago. The figures were printed in red, black, and brown, and, because of the almost complete absence of light in the cavern, the colors are as vivid as if recently applied. How many men of today could duplicate the work?
Copyright, National Geographic Society. Reproduced by special permission.

lutionists do, that the Neanderthal race was far older than the Cro-Magnons. The two may, for all the evidence to the contrary, have been practically contemporary. The way in which men like Hrdlicka assign to the recovered skulls and bones their respective places as relatively near or far from the present date is to make the assumption that man has evolved slowly from some ape-form, and then give to those bones that have the more unintelligent aspect the more remote position and those that have the more intelligent aspect the more near position. This, however, is purely arbitrary and foolish.

It may well be granted by the lover of the Scriptures

that man has a greater antiquity than the commonly supposed 4000 B.C. It is the conviction of the writer that the genealogies of the Bible form no basis whatever for fixing the date of the creation of Adam. It is his belief that the genealogies of the Old Testament were meant to teach not lengths but lines of descent. For all the Scriptures testify to the contrary, man may be 50,000 or 100,-000 years old. No one knows how old man is. [138a]

THE EFFORT TO FILL IN THE SPIRITUAL GAP BETWEEN MEN AND ANIMALS

Man has a spiritual nature which distinguishes him widely from the dumb brute. But for the consistent evolutionist to account for the distinction, God is not needed. He is not wanted. He cannot be permitted to enter into the process of evolution without acknowledging the *principle* of a supernatural creation of distinct species to be correct. Since, therefore, any interference in the evolutionary process from a supernatural Divine source is excluded by logical necessity, it is said by evolutionists that the soul of man, like his body, is the product of purely natural operations of the laws of nature.

That there is a wide gap between men and animals in their mental and moral natures has been recognized even by the heathen from Aristotle to the present time. The savage instinctively recognizes the existence of this difference and feels his superiority over the whole animal creation. This feeling of lordship is due to the presence in man of a spiritual nature created after God's image.

It is recognized by evolutionists that the spiritual gulf between man, the crown of creation, and animals must be filled in without recourse to a supernatural power, or be so narrowed that it can be said that the transition from brute instincts and consciousness to human intellectual and moral powers was easily accomplished by the natural forces producing evolution. In seeking to accomplish this task two schools of evolutionary psychologists have sprung up. One is the school which seeks to humanize the brute, raising him up as high as possible in the sphere of in-

---

[138a] See chapter on Biblical Chronology in *Before Abraham.*

144

telligence and morals. The other is the school which seeks to brutize the human, pulling man down if possible until he meets the highest level to which the animal can be raised. The first of these schools is represented by Romanes, who has written *Mental Evolution in the Animal World,* the second by McCabe, who has written *Evolution of Mind.* All such attempts to bridge the gap, however, have been unsuccessful.

The practice of humanizing the brute is one that has gone on among men unconsciously for ages and, until the rise of the modern anti-Biblical philosophy of evolution, was without harm. It consists in doing to animals what every little girl does with her dolls, i. e., reads into them her own mental processes. A dog, for example, that has been soundly whipped for taking food from the table, when it is discovered in the act of doing so again, slinks away with its tail between its legs. Whereupon it is said to be "ashamed." Men shift their own mental and moral processes into the brute, attribute to it the power of reason as well as their own feelings.

Stories of animal intelligence are related by the thousands. Dog stories are fascinating and popular reading. As Prof. Thorndike says, "Human folks, as a matter of fact, are eager to find intelligence in animals. They like to." [139] If a stranger visits a home where is kept a dog which has learned to open the gate by jumping up and bumping the latch with its nose, the stranger's first impulse is to credit the dog with intelligence like his own. "A smart dog, that," he will say. Whereupon the owner, who has observed the long process of irrational jumping, scratching, and howling at the gate, the thwarted random efforts in every direction, the final accidental hitting of the latch and the resultant success, will rather disgustingly grunt, "Uh-uh." An excited little chick, feeding, may peck at a wasp and get stung. Its abstinence from pecking wasps in the future is likely to be attributed to such a logical syllogism as this, "That object has a striking resemblance to the thing that stung me yesterday. Now I don't want to be stung today, therefore I shall leave

[139] *Animal Intelligence,* page 24.

that thing alone." The one who so attributes reasoning powers to the little creature may not know, however, that chicks are instinctively afraid of wasps when they recognize them as such. To illustrate the marvelous intelligence characteristic of animal species tales are told of long journeys home made by domestic creatures which have been lost. Nothing, however, is said about the countless examples of animal stupidity, of their mechanical and thoughtless lives, of their fundamental bestial natures. "Thousands of cats on thousands of occasions sit helplessly yowling and no one takes thought of it to write to his friend, the professor; but let one claw at the knob of a door supposedly in order to be let out, and straightway this cat becomes the representative of the cat mind in all books." [140]

It is, however, when this humanizing of the brute, this shifting of the human range of thought into the brain of the animal, is done for the purpose of overthrowing the Bible that it must be exposed and opposed. It is impossible to trace any marked gradations of intelligence through the animals to man. The ape is no more essentially intelligent than the cat or dog. Being more physically active and restless than the dog or cat, and having a structure of fore and hind feet that permits him to make a greater variety of physical movements, the monkey can learn to accomplish a greater variety of tricks than the dog or cat. Essentially, however, the ape is no more intelligent. In some respects the ant is superior to either the dog, cat, or ape. No animal, however, has the capacity to reason, by which is meant the capacity to handle abstract ideas. As Prof. F. O. Jenkins says,[141] "What dog or ape that warms himself by the fire and has seen wood put onto it time and again ever has sense enough to bring sticks of wood to it himself when he sees it dying out and feels himself getting cold?" To which might be added what dog or ape would ever have sense enough to make a match, or to perform acts based on algebra or geometry, or have the impulse to build

---

[140] Thorndike, *Animal Intelligence,* page 25.
[141] *Princeton Theological Review,* April, 1924. Prof. Jenkins is the only anti-evolutionist quoted in this book.

146

temples and bury the dead? The conclusion of Prof. Thorndike,[142] after years spent in the study of animal psychology, including two years when he had under personal observation three monkeys, is worth notice. It is this, "There is also in the case of the monkey as in that of the other animals positive evidence of the absence of any general function of reasoning." [143]

The other method of filling the gap, i. e., brutizing man, is a practice of recent origin. It sprang up with the theory of biological evolution. It consists in citing those instances in which members of the human race have become basely degraded and live in a coarse and rude state of barbarism, claiming that these men have small intellectual and moral powers and represent stages of evolution but little removed from the brute. Often cited as an example of this is that savage tribe of men called the Tasmanians, which became extinct fifty years ago, of whom it is said they could not count and had practically no language. McCabe, an evolutionist most active in attempting to fill the gap between animal and man, admits that the Tasmanians died out "before exact and searching inquiry was made into their qualities." [144]

Having read in an earlier edition of this book about McCabe's views, Rev. H. G. Scholefield of Australia wrote to the author as follows: "As one whose ancestors had something to do with these people, I am in a position to state that it is not true to say that they could not count; they counted in series of tens, and could estimate accurately the number of sheep in a flock. I have carefully examined the plaster cast of the head of Truganini, the last of the Tasmanian blacks, and can understand why Prof. Baldwin Spencer, who knew more about the blacks both in Tasmania and on the mainland of Australia than any other anthropologist, described her as having been a woman of fairly high intelligence. It is just as well that McCabe admitted that the Tasmanians died out before exact and searching inquiry was made into their qualities, for the

[142] Prof. of Psychology in Columbia University.
[143] *Columbia University Contributions to Philosophy, Psychology, and Education*, page 14.
[144] *Evolution of Mind*, page 265.

recent researches into the habits and culture of the Australian blacks, both in Tasmania and on the mainland, confirm the truth of the following statement by the writer of an article 'Australia' in *Chambers Encylopedia:* 'Nothing is more common, or more condemnable among writers on Australia, than the careless adoption of ill-informed and unobservant descriptions of the "blackfellow" given by early white settlers. Given a community cut off from the world while still in the hunter stage of civilization, and pent in a country none of whose animals lend themselves to domestication, it is hardly possible to conceive of a way of living more skillfully and intelligently adapted to the environment than is that of the native Australian uninfluenced by the white invasion.' McCabe is welcome to any help for his theory he can get by studying the Australian aborigines. Given a like environment, perhaps McCabe would not have risen so high in the scale of civilization as the despised Tasmanian black."

Potentially all men are alike. The children of the lowest savage tribes existing, when separated from their native environment and brought under the influence of Christian teachers, become men and women of the noblest human type. Beneath the surface of corruption and degradation into which men have sunk, and there is abundant evidence that the progress of all savage tribes has been downward, not upward, there is that in them which inspired the keen observer Shakespeare to say, "What a piece of work is man! How noble in reason! How infinite in faculty! In form, in moving, how express and admirable! In apprehension how like a god! The beauty of the world! The paragon of animals!" [145]

In spite of every effort of evolutionists to fill the mental and spiritual gap between man and the brute, this gulf, like the physiological gulf, remains. This fact is acknowledged by so prominent an evolutionist as Vernon Kellogg, who, writing in *World's Work* for March, 1926, in an article entitled "Some Things Science Doesn't Know," says there are things scientific men cannot explain. They are the origin of life, the causes of evolution, and the cause

---

[145] *Hamlet,* Act II, Scene II.

of the spiritual gap between man and the brute. The existence of this gulf he admits. He cannot, however, as a thorough-going evolutionist, admit the existence of it to be due to a supernatural, creative act of God, for to do so would open the door for a flood of creative acts between species which could not logically be kept out.

Romanes was the great apostle at the opening of this century of the evolution of the human spirit from animal instincts. His work on the evolution of animal intelligence is a classic among evolutionists of this day and is much read and quoted by them. Few who read his book and are influenced by it, however, are aware of the fact that in the closing days of his life Romanes renounced all he had said and acknowledged his spiritual endowment to be due to a creative act of God. Before Romanes died he returned to a full Christian belief.[146]

SUMMARY

The "missing-links" are unsatisfactory evidences of human evolution because (1) too much suspicion and uncertainty surrounds them, (2) only those ancient human remains that serve the evolutionary purpose are offered as proofs. Those ancient human remains that work against the theory of evolution are rejected. (3) Those human remains offered as proof of evolution are not essentially different from human skeletons of today.

Consistent evolutionists must explain the origin of the human spirit in the same way they explain the origin of the human body.

The evolutionist seeks to fill the spiritual gap between man and the brute by (1) seeking to raise the brute to the level of man by attributing to the brute human, spiritual powers (the attempt fails because the brute cannot be shown to have those powers), and (2) by seeking to pull man down to the level of the brute by pointing out the brutishness of certain savage tribes. The baseness of low heathen peoples, however, is due to a fall from a higher moral and intellectual plane to a lower one. The basest savages are truly human.

[146] See *Life and Letters* by his wife.

Conclusion

In the preceding pages all the standards proofs of evolution have been presented and discussed. It may seem to the reader that these proofs are not so impressive as he has been led to expect from the fact that many highly educated men are evolutionists, and a suspicion may have arisen that the proofs have not been fairly presented. It is well for the lover of the Bible to know, therefore, what is the real reason why many educated men accept evolution as the explanation of the present world of plants and animals. The reason is not the overwhelming nature of the evidence. Many evolutionists grant the weakness of the theory they put forward. But, disliking the philosophy which underlies the idea of creation, and being unable or unwilling, for moral or intellectual reasons, to accept the fact that there exists a God who might have created living species by definite, supernatural, spontaneous acts, these men rule out creation as a possibility, and, having no other choice, are forced to hold that things came by themselves or evolved, in spite of all the difficulties.

That dislike of the idea of creation is in fact the underlying reason for belief in evolution by many leading evolutionists is apparent from the following statements of evolutionists. Prof. Louis T. More of the University of Cincinnati says, "When we examine the causes of our belief [in evolution] we find that, excepting our *desire to eliminate special creation and, generally, what we call the miraculous,* most of them can be considered only as secondary proofs to confirm a theory already advanced."[147] He also says, "Our faith in the idea of evolution depends

[147] *Dogma of Evolution*—lectures delivered at Princeton University in January, 1925, page 117.

150

on our *reluctance to accept the antagonistic doctrine of special creation.*" [148] Prof. Bateson, who, on account of his high standing in the scientific world, often angered his fellow evolutionists by his frank confessions of the weaknesses of the theory, said, "The evolution theory finds its support *not in direct observation, but in the difficulty of forming an alternate hypothesis.*" [149] On one notable occasion [150] Bateson, at the close of an address entitled "Evolutionary Faith and Modern Doubts," in which he had made some surprising acknowledgments of the weakness of the theory, showed his contempt for the Biblical idea of creation in these words, "When such confessions are made, the enemies of science [believers in the Bible are not enemies of science, but of science 'falsely so-called'] see their chance. If we cannot declare here and now how species arose, they will obligingly offer us the solutions with which obscurantism is satisfied (i. e., creation). Let us then proclaim in precise and unmistakable language that our faith in evolution remains unshaken. . . . The obscurantist [a term of derision applied to the creationist] has *nothing to suggest which is worth a moment's attention.*" And on still another occasion [151] he said what unavoidably arouses the suspicion that the advocacy by some scientific men of the theory of evolution as against the truth of the Bible has somewhat of a moral basis. While speaking on heredity, but upholding throughout his address the idea of evolution, Bateson said, "Whether we like it or not, extraordinary and far-reaching changes in public opinion are coming to pass. Man is just beginning to know himself for what he is—a rather long-lived animal, with great powers of enjoyment if he does not deliberately forego them. Hitherto superstition and mythical ideas of sin have predominantly controlled these powers. Mysticism will not die out; for these

[148] *Dogma of Evolution*—lectures delivered at Princeton University in January, 1925, page 304.

[149] *Materials for the Study of Variation,* page 4.

[150] An address delivered before the American Association for the Advancement of Science at Toronto in 1922, *Science,* Jan. 20, 1922.

[151] Presidential address before the British Association for the Advancement of Science in Australia, 1914. *Smithsonian Institute Report,* 1915, page 359.

strange fancies knowledge is no cure; but their forms change, and mysticism as a force for the oppression of joy is *happily* losing its hold on the modern world." The reference in this quotation is undoubtedly to the Scriptural record of the fall of man and the teaching of the Bible regarding sin and its punishment.

A word in conclusion on the relation of the theory of evolution to the religion of the Bible might not be considered amiss. Two opposing philosophies meet when the philosophy of evolution and the philosophy of Biblical Christianity come together, and it may be said that no mental gymnastics, however skilful, can ever reconcile the two. They lock horns at every turn.

Biblical Christianity has as its chief cornerstone the existence of a personal, Divine Being, who has in various ways and at sundry times broken into the ordinary course of nature with supernatural manifestations of His power, and who can at any time break in again. This is the *sine qua non* of orthodox Christianity. The philosophy of evolution, however, has no welcome place for the supernatural. While Divine interference in the process of evolution is required at the present time for a satisfactory explanation of the origin of life and the human soul, and is called in by certain evolutionists to help the theory over hard places, the tendency is to rule out any such outside interference entirely. In the words of the evolutionist, August Weismann, "The conception of an evolution of life upon the earth reaches far beyond the bounds of any single science and influences our whole realm of thought. It means nothing less than the elimination of the miraculous from our knowledge of nature." [152]

According to Biblical Christianity the human race began its existence as a single pair created in a state of moral and physical perfection. This state of perfection was lost to the race when the first pair disobeyed the injunctions of the Creator. According to Biblical Christianity evil acts committed by man are the fruits of moral depravity, and whosoever commits them is guilty and punishable by God. In the light of the theory of evolu-

---

[152] Locy, *Biology and Its Makers,* page 367.

152

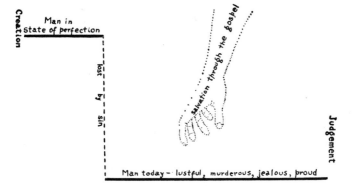

Fig. 54. *Christian Doctrine:* Man was created perfect in body and spirit. Through sin man's original perfection was lost and man is now a "fallen" creature. Salvation is individual, through repentance and faith in Jesus Christ. The consummation of all earthly affairs is judgment.

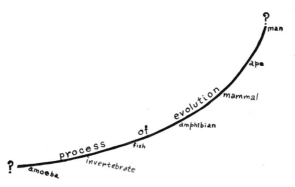

Fig. 55. *Evolutionary Doctrine:* Humanity's progress has ever been upward. Physically and spiritually man is at the highest point in human history. There has been no "fall"; consequently there is no need for a redeemer. Since the natural process which evolution is can not produce a supernatural, immortal spirit there is no individual salvation.

153

tion, however, mankind is today at the highest point in its history. Man is the nearest to moral perfection he has ever been, and is steadily improving. What the orthodox Christian calls sin is, in the light of evolution, mere error or shortcoming due to incompletion in man's make-up Evolutionary philosophy would change the Bible statement "The soul that sinneth it shall die" to read: "The soul that sinneth is striving for higher life."

Biblical Christianity answers the question which Jesus asked the Pharisees, "If David called him [i. e., the Christ] Lord, how is he his son" by answering that Jesus Christ is the *God* of David, and his *son* also, because Jesus Christ is the God-man, Creator and creature united in one mysterious person by the miraculous operation of the Holy Spirit through a virgin birth. Since, however, nothing so supernatural as a virgin birth is consistently allowed in world affairs by evolutionary philosophy, he who is called Jesus Christ can at best be but a man like unto his brethren, the product of the same evolutionary operation by which they were produced. By the same necessity—that of excluding supernatural interferences in natural processes—the resurrection and ascension of Jesus is also excluded. Nor can He, by the same token, be the object of God's wrath, self-substituted to bear the guilt and punishment of men, but must be merely an example to the race to lead it on in evolution to a higher hill. In fact, an atoning Savior is not needed in evolutionary doctrine.

According to Biblical Christianity the Bible is a supernatural revelation of God, given to men through human instruments, of things mankind could only vaguely surmise were they not revealed. It is a Divine revelation to man of the origin, present condition, and destiny of the human race. Without this Word of God man is left to his own ever-changing speculations for guidance upon the sea of existence. According to the philosophy of evolution the Bible is no more supernatural or inspired than the works of Emerson or Shakespeare. The teachings it contains are merely the conclusions of men of an untutored age concerning things on which the light of modern intelligence had not been shed.

Here is the crux of the whole matter. Is the Bible the word of man or the Word of God? We contend for the latter and say that if the Bible is not inspired, it is truly remarkable that an untutored man like Moses, never having attended a modern university, said to have been scarcely more than a savage, living in an unscientific age, should state a biological principle of heredity so in accord with the latest scientific biological discoveries. *"After its kind, whose seed is in itself,"* is as good an expression of the *central principle of Mendel's Laws* as can be made. It is no small task to explain satisfactorily why a writer of so remote a day as that in which the writer of the Book of Genesis lived, if he were not inspired from an outside source to do so, should go to the trouble of repeating eight times in half a chapter the biological rule that species were created to reproduce only themselves. Christian believers can rest their case for the inspiration of the Bible and the truth of Christianity on the words of Genesis, "After its kind."

Appendix I

NATURAL SPECIES*

Up until the time of Darwin all men who thought about the matter at all recognized that there were such things as natural species. The idea came from two sources, from the Scriptures and from observation of nature. The Scriptures taught that all men were descended from Adam and Eve, which gave the concept of mankind as constituting a natural species of the highest order. The Scriptures taught that two of a "kind" (Hebrew MIN, Genesis 1:11, 6:20) entered the ark as seed for a new animal population on the earth after the Deluge, which gave the idea of the existence of natural species among the animals. These simple but enlightening Scriptural facts were the original source of the commonly held opinion that there were natural species. Observation of nature confirmed this view. It was apparent to men that mankind itself was made up of many races and types scattered the world over, yet that all these races were perfectly able to intermarry and bear children, except in a few individual cases. Man became to himself, therefore, from observation of nature, the best example of a natural species. It was readily apparent also that among the animals there were similar forms which cross-bred naturally with one another and produced fertile progeny. In the cases of dogs, horses, cattle, sheep, poultry this was so. All these formed groups which contained many varieties of individuals, all of which readily and easily crossed with the individuals within their respective groups. In plants the knowledge that there were natural species was not so clearly recognized. The knowledge which the ancients had 800 years before Christ regarding the sexuality of plants had been lost during the Middle Ages, and was not recovered until the latter part of the 17th century. But when the fact that plants as well as animals cross-bred was rediscovered, and experimentation in the crossing of plants was carried out, men readily concluded that what was true in the animal kingdom was true also in the plant world. So up until 1860 the existence of natural species was a conviction of all intelligent men. This is evident from the definitions of species given by men of science of those days. Linnaeus (1707-1778) said, "There are as many species as God created in

*Numbers in parentheses refer to the sources of information listed at the end of the appendix.

156

the beginning," and this he amplified by saying. "Varieties are plants of the same species." John Ray (1628-1705) defined natural species as "a group of organisms with marked characteristics in common and freely inter-breeding." Baron Cuvier (1761-1832) said, "All the beings belonging to one of these forms [perpetual since the beginning of all things, that is, the Creation], constitute what we call species." De Candolle (1778-1841) defined species as "an assemblage of all the individuals which resemble each other more than they do others, which can by mutual fecundation produce fertile individuals, and which are able to reproduce their like in a manner that they may be supposed by analogy to have descended from a single being or a single pair." Quatrefages (1810-1892) called species "an assemblage of individuals more or less resembling one another, which are descended or may be regarded as being descended from a single pair by the uninterrupted succession of families."

The criterion in the minds of intelligent men before Darwin of what constituted a natural species was the natural ability and willingness to cross-breed and produce fertile offspring. Members of groups called species crossed with one another in nature and produced fertile progeny, whereas distinct species did not cross, or, if they were induced to do so by man, the progeny manifested greater or lesser degrees of sterility. There were two especially famous botanists before Darwin. One was Kohlreuter, who between the years 1760 and 1766 performed the first series of systematic experiments in plant-crossing carried out in modern times. So thorough and well-recorded was his work that exactly the same results have been secured by those who have repeated his experiments since 1900. The other was Gartner, who is said to have performed between the years 1825 and 1850, experiments in cross-breeding plants "that have not been equalled by any modern worker" (2). These two men, after their years of investigation, concluded emphatically that natural species composed of inter-breeding varieties exist, and that between distinct natural species some degree of sterility was a universal law of nature.

The view of men before Darwin's day regarding natural species is well stated by the evolutionist, de Vries: "At his (Darwin's) time it was universally assumed that species had been created as such, but that subspecies and varieties had been derived from them according to natural laws" (10).

DENIAL OF THE EXISTENCE OF NATURAL SPECIES.—The believer in the Bible need not hesitate one moment to accept what is and has always been so obvious. Natural species most certainly do exist, and there is no real ground for thinking that they have not been and will not always exist as they are today. The lover of the Bible can expect, however, that not merely the constancy but even the existence of species will be denied or discredited by many evolutionists as a part of their efforts to discredit the Biblical doctrine of special creation.

The first denial of the existence of natural species was made by

Charles Darwin in the *Origin of Species,* published 1859. He taught that natural species, while they seem to exist, were but figments of men's imaginations and did not exist in reality. The reason he taught thus was because the blotting out of the idea of natural species was absolutely necessary to the successful propagation of his theory of evolution. This is apparent from the words of his close friend, Alfred Russel Wallace, written fifteen years after the publication of the *Origin.* "One of the greatest, perhaps we may say the greatest of all difficulties in the way of accepting the theory of evolution as the complete explanation of the origin of species has been the remarkable difference between varieties and species in respect of fertility when crossed. Generally speaking, it may be said that varieties of any species, however different they may be in external appearance, are perfectly fertile when crossed and their mongrel offspring are equally fertile when bred among themselves; while distinct species, on the other hand, however closely they may resemble each other externally, are usually infertile when crossed, and their hybrid offspring absolutely sterile" (17). To get rid of the conception of species which was accepted by scientists and others of his day was, therefore, in Darwin's opinion, absolutely necessary. Instead of definite species being in existence, organic life had to be in a state of flux with no specific distinctions whatever. Darwin eagerly sought, therefore, both in the *Origin* and his later volumes, *Plants and Animals Under Domestication,* to blot out the idea of natural species. And the substance of his argument for doing so was that species do not exist because there is not always the same degree of sterility between them. He said, "Why has the production of hybrids been permitted (by the Creator)? To grant to species the special power of producing hybrids, and then stop their further propagation by different degrees of sterility . . . seems a strange arrangement."

EQUAL DEGREES OF STERILITY BETWEEN SPECIES NOT ESSENTIAL TO THEIR EXISTENCE.—To the question Darwin asks it may well be replied, "Why should the production of hybrids not be permitted?" Because a thing happens to be a "strange arrangement" to Darwin does not mean there is not a very excellent and wonderful reason for just that arrangement. Darwin evidently thought the Lord would have done better if He had consulted him on some matters. Alas! He did not, and therefore we find natural species separated by different degrees of sterility.

This arrangement, however, which we know exists, furnishes a hollow argument for the non-existence of natural species. For the existence and perpetuation of species some degree of sterility partial or total is, of course, necessary. Unless some sterility between species had been caused to exist, interbreeding between the various "kinds" would have taken place in such a way that utter chaos and disorder would now have been the result. But all that was actually necessary, both for the existence and perpetuation of species was that between them there should be a sufficient degree of sterility to keep disorder and chaos out of the world and to keep natural species reproducing "after their kind." That such a degree of sterility actually exists all who have eyes to see can see.

OUTWARD APPEARANCE NOT A SURE CRITERION OF NATURAL SPECIES.—Doubtless there are many tests which are yet to be discovered by which natural species may be distinguished. One present test is outward form. Members of the same species look alike. Beneath a varying outward appearance the different varieties of a species have an underlying similarity which usually enables men to decide which forms belong to a species and which do not. Outward form, however, while it is of much assistance in determining what is a natural species and what is not, is by itself an insufficient test for the reason that organisms which may look alike outwardly are very often very different germinally (i. e. in the constitution of the gametes or "marrying cells"). For example, there are many varieties of the ass, which are all readily cross fertile with one another. There are also many varieties of the horse, which are all readily cross fertile with one another. One variety of the ass group looks considerably like the Prevalski breed of horse. The Prevalski horse, however, and the ass are so different germinally that the offspring of a cross, the mule, is sterile. It has likewise been discovered that horses have 19 chromosomes in their gametes, while asses have 32 (13). On the other hand, two breeds of horses, a great Clydesdale and a slim racing Thoroughbred look so different that it would be easy to class them as different natural species. Yet they have an identical constitution of gametes. Appearances, therefore, are deceitful. Two moths, one called Euralia Wahlbergi and the other Euralia mima, look so different that, on the basis of looks alone they would be classed as different species. Yet they are perfectly fertile when mated (15). On the other hand there are two distinct groups of fertile, interbreeding fruit-flies, Drosophila Melanogaster and Drosophila Simulans, which look much alike when not examined closely. But these can be made to cross only with great difficulty and the hybrids are absolutely sterile (14). There are two barleys, one having six rows, the other having two rows of kernels. These are, therefore, on the basis of appearance likely to be classed as distinct species. These two barleys, however, cross readily and produce offspring according to Mendel's Law. What is called "teosinte," a variety of wild corn found in hot countries like Mexico, is called on the basis of appearance a species distinct from the natural species, corn, of which there are hundreds of interbreeding varieties differing in size, shape, color and other characteristics. But since teosinte and the corn varieties are perfectly interfertile there is no reason for putting teosinte in a natural species by itself (5). Who would hastily think, merely by looking at them, that "cabbage" forms shown in Figure 2 are so readily interfertile as to constitute one natural species.

STERILITY ONE IMPORTANT CRITERION OF SPECIES.—As already

indicated, one of the principal tests of species has to do with the phenomenon of sterility, and with the kind or character of the sterility even more than the degree. Professor D. F. Jones of Yale University says, "One criterion that divides living organisms into natural groups is the barrier of sexual incompatibility. There can be no argument about the separate classification of a race that cannot unite with other organisms and produce fertile off-spring" (13).

COMPLETE STERILITY BETWEEN SPECIES THE RULE.—The animal and plant world is made up of thousands of groups of varieties[153] which are perfectly fertile with one another, but which are absolutely sterile toward members of all other groups. Cases are reported of complete fertility between "distinct" species. This, say Babcock and Clausen, is "a comparatively rare condition" (1). Such reported cases arise from the fact that different varieties within species have been mistaken for distinct species purely on the basis of outward appearance. The general truth is just the opposite. Complete sterility between species is the rule, and any degree of fertility between them is the exception. How did this acknowledged condition come about? Here is a problem over which evolutionists have long pondered for a satisfactory explanation, but in vain.

Darwin in his day, and his followers today, however, make much of those comparatively few cases where the sterility between certain distinct species is not complete but partial. A few typical examples of such cases may be considered, and the reader left to decide for himself whether these cases weaken the idea of the existence of natural species or strengthen it.

CASES OF INCOMPLETE STERILITY BETWEEN DISTINCT SPECIES.—There are several hundred varieties of apples which have been developed by man, and all these are perfectly interfertile. Apples will cross with no other species. Attempts have been made to cross the apple with the pear and the quince, but such attempts have failed utterly. There are many varieties of the species to which cabbage belongs, and these varieties are all so readily fertile with one another that it is hard to keep a cabbage field of one variety pure if it is near the field of another. Cabbages will not cross with the two species which are most similar to them, turnip and rape. Yet a Russian named Krapechenko (1928) managed to get a cabbage pollen to fertilize a radish ovum (11). From this there came a plant monstrosity which grew and grew in the green-house, but was never able to produce a flower. The germ cells

---

153 The number of varieties of domestic plant and animal species, is, in general, much greater than that of the species known only in the wild state, which are sometimes represented by but one or two varieties. The reason for this is that in the domesticated species the new varieties which have arisen have been sheltered from destruction by man and used for his benefit, whereas many of the new varieties which have arisen in the natural state have been unable to survive when they appeared. It is extremely probable that most wild species have the same capacity for producing varieties which our domestic species, e. g. horses, cattle, pigs, chickens, sheep, have displayed.

of the two distinct species, cabbage and radish, were able to unite, and the different elements in the germ cells were elastic enough to adjust themselves to one another sufficiently well to produce a plant body, but were not able to adjust themselves well enough together to produce such delicate and vital structures as the flowers (see page 171).[154] Strawberries and blackberries are distinct species with many varieties of each. Luther Burbank succeeded in making a cross between a strawberry and a blackberry. A peculiar hybrid was produced. At first it grew exactly like a strawberry. Then it changed and grew like a raspberry. "But no seed was formed. The plants were as sterile as mules" (5). After "ten thousand tries" Burbank got a plant from a cross of a petunia with an ornamental nicotiana plant. The hybrid grew peculiarly, first like a nicotiana, and then like a petunia. The hybrid, however, was completely sterile (5). Wheat varieties, of which there are hundreds cannot be readily crossed with anything but wheat. However, this, for example, is reported. A man named Jesenko made several thousands of attempts to pollinate rye flowers with wheat pollen, but in vain. Then he tried to pollinate wheat flowers with rye pollen, and he managed to get seeds at the rate of six for each one thousand attempts. These seeds produced hybrid rye-wheat plants with flowers, but the plants were incapable by themselves of producing offspring. Jesenko continued his experiments by trying to cross the rye-wheat hybrid back with either parent form. When the hybrid was pollinated with wheat pollen three seeds were secured in 1,000 attempts, and when the hybrids were pollinated with rye pollen only one seed was secured in 4,800 attempts (13). What happened to these hybrid progeny will presently be explained.

Animals likewise shed rich light on the difficulties of sterility which arise when distinct species are crossed. Dogs and foxes will not cross at all, nor will the quite similar species, sheep and goats. The horse and the ass will cross, but the product, a mule, is sterile. The reason for the well known sterility of the mule has also been discovered. The germ cells of the horse have 19 chromosomes. The gametes of the ass have 32. In spite of this difference a union of the germ cells takes place and a new and useful individual is formed. But when growth and development of the new individual proceeds to the point where new germ cells are to be formed for reproduction, confusion and disorder take place within the germ cells and the mules are sterile. "When the hybrid mule forms its germ cells, the chromosomes do not pair or balance properly, and the resulting cells are not able to sur-

---

154 Cabbages, according to evolutionary theory, are closely related to the turnip and the rape. All three species are supposed to have evolved out of the same branch on the evolutionary tree, and are therefore classed in the same genus (Brassica). Radishes, because they are so different from the cabbage, rape, and turnip, are supposed to have come from a totally different branch of the evolutionary tree. Yet cabbage and radishes will form hybrids, while cabbages and their near relatives, rapes and turnips, will not. Surely here is a "strange arrangement." How would Darwin explain it? Radishes and cabbages each have the same number of chromosomes (9) while rapes and turnips do not.

vive" (16). The ass and the zebra will cross, but the product, an ass-zebra hybrid, is sterile (13). American bison have been crossed with domestic cattle. The cross can occur only when the cattle is the male. The "cattalo," as the hybrid is sometimes called, is very hard to produce. The cross is described as "violent" and "dangerously severe." About two-thirds of the hybrids are born dead. The mothers of the hybrids themselves often die. Of the small number of hybrids that are produced alive very few are males, and these die early. Only one male "cattalo" is ever known to have reached maturity, and it was as sterile as the mule. Females only usually reach maturity, and not many of these. Most of these females are sterile, but in some cases by crossing them with either domestic or bison bulls a few three-quarter hybrids have been produced. These hybrids are still inclined to be sterile. When the back-crossing of the hybrids with the one or the other parent species is kept up for a few generations, the sterility entirely disappears, as well as the physical characteristics of the other natural species, a phenomenon the importance of which will presently be called to the reader's attention (4).

From the above examples it is apparent that there is some inherent quality in the germ cells of different groups of both plants and animals of distinct species which enables them to unite and function normally and easily with the members of their own group, but which makes them unable to unite and function normally with members of the other groups.

HYBRIDS BETWEEN TRUE SPECIES UNSTABLE ORGANISMS WHICH REVERT TO PARENT SPECIES.—A highly significant light on the existence and permanence of natural species comes from the consideration of what happens when two distinct species are able to cross and produce a few offsprings that are partially fertile. What happens is that the hybrids revert to one or the other natural species, and the intermediate forms no longer exist. The progeny of interspecific hybrids split into two groups, and these groups more or less gradually become identical with the original species which produced them, all the hybrids eventually ceasing to be. The split into groups may not come in the exact middle. In some cases the hybrid progeny all form one group, like one or the other parent species, and go only in one direction, that is revert to just one or the other parent species. The final result, however, is always the same. The hybrids eventually cease to exist. Professors Babcock and Clausen say, "It has often been observed that the progenies of partially fertile hybrids run back to the parental condition" (1).

REVERSION IN RYE-WHEAT HYBRIDS.—As an example of the reversion to natural species spoken of above may be taken the case of the cross between rye and wheat. The rye-wheat hybrid produced is a highly sterile plant. It is not able to reproduce itself. The cause of the sterility is the even balance of elements foreign to each other. The only way any offspring from the rye-wheat hybrids can be produced is by back-crossing them with either rye or wheat. with the result that a limited number of plants are secured. However, the hybrid offspring produced by such back-crossing are practically identical with the natural species with which the back-crossing is done. The hybrids crossed with wheat produce plants that are like wheat. The hybrids crossed with rye produce plants that are like rye. These plants, however, are not all equally like the parent form with which the back-crossing is done. Some are more so than others. Plants produced by back-crossing the hybrids with rye are strikingly like rye, but some more so than others. Plants produced by back-crossing the hybrids with wheat are strikingly like wheat, only some are more so than others. And, what is important to note, the plants most like the parent species with which the back-crossing is done are most fertile, while the plants least like the parent species with which the back-crossing is done are most sterile. Furthermore the hybrid progeny which are most like wheat are fertile toward wheat and sterile toward rye, and the hybrid progeny most like rye are fertile toward rye and sterile toward wheat. The sterile plants, because of their sterility, die out. The fertile plants, because of their fertility, live on, and each succeeding generation becomes more and more like the species they are closest to. The final result is that the hybrids return to the natural species out of which they sprang (13).

REVERSION IN CATTLE-BISON HYBRIDS.—We have already referred to the production of the hybrids between domestic cattle and bison and the difficulties of the cross. The male hybrids are invariably sterile; the females partially fertile. Since no males are fertile, back-crossing must be done with either domestic or bison males. But when this takes place, the hybrids show a great tendency to reversion even after but one cross, while in two back-crosses the reversion is practically complete. Mossom Boyd, a wealthy cattleman who performed long experiments in crossing bison and domestic cattle in hopes of producing a hardier type of beef-cattle for the western ranges, says, "An ordinary observer might mistake the three-quarter buffalo (the product of a cattle-bison hybrid back-crossed with a bison) for a bison; he would scarcely distinguish the one-quarter buffalo (the product of a cattle-bison hybrid back-crossed with a domestic male) from domestic cattle, except for the finer quality of hair. The one-eighth buffaloes he would not distinguish at all from domestic cattle" (4). It was this instability in cattle-bison hybrids and their tendency to reversion which caused W. F. Hornaday, Director, of the New York Zoological Gardens, to say in 1904, "Interesting as have been the experiments made by Mr. C. J. Jones and others in the cross-breeding of buffaloes (bison) and domestic cattle, it is now quite time that all such experiments should cease. It has been proven conclusively that it is impossible to introduce and maintain a tangible strain of buffalo blood into the mass of western range cattle" (12).

163

REVERSION IN WILD CAVY-GUINEA PIG HYBRIDS.—From 1909 to 1914 Professor Detlefsen of Illinois University carried on a series of experiments in the crossing of the common guinea-pig with a species of wild rodents from Brazil, which illustrates well the phenomena of reversion in species crosses. The wild Brazilian cavy is somewhat like the guinea-pig, but has certain differences in physical characteristics and is only half as large. The two species were crossed with difficulty because of their instinctive aversion for one another, similar to the natural aversion of the two species, cattle and bison. It is certain that the species we are discussing would never mate in nature, so great is their distaste for one another. As in the case of the cattle-bison hybrids, the male hybrids of this cavy-guinea pig cross were sterile. The female hybrids were fertile. A back-cross was made between a female hybrid and a wild cavy. All the offspring of this cross were sterile, so such back-crossing with cavies was discontinued. The hybrids were then crossed with guinea-pig males. The three-quarter male offspring produced by this crossing were still all sterile, the female offspring fertile. These three-quarter hybrid females were again back-crossed with the guinea pigs, and in this generation a few of the male offspring produced were fertile, although most of them were still sterile. The females, of course, were fertile. By continued back-crossing with guinea pigs the male offspring gradually returned to normal fertility. By that time, however, all trace of any physical characteristics of the Brazilian cavy had long disappeared. In fact after only two back-crosses with guinea pigs the hybrids were indistinguishable from normal guinea pigs in size, skeletal shape, and coat colors (9).

Further interesting light on the instability of interspecific hybrids and their reversion to either species entering into a cross comes from the consideration of what happens when two distinct species are able to cross and produce offspring without recourse to back-crossing with either parent species. Such cases are rare and are known only in plants, but when they occur they furnish more evidence of the fact that hybrids between natural species are not stable organisms and eventually revert to one or the other species in the cross.

REVERSION IN RUSTICA AND PANICULATA.—As an example of such reversion may be taken the case of the hybrids produced by crossing the two species of ornamental plans technically known as Nicotiana Rustica and N. Naniculata. The experiment about to be described was performed and recorded by Prof. E. M. East of Harvard University. When N. Rustica and N. Paniculata were crossed, almost complete sterility was observed. About one seed was produced where normally there should have been a hundred. These seeds produced plants on which, by careful hand pollination, a few shriveled seeds were formed. Many of these shriveled seeds were sterile, but a few germinated and produced plants. By hard work 246 such second-generation, hybrid plants were secured. But a noteworthy condition among these plants was evi-

164

dent. They were divided into two groups, one group resembling one natural species, the other group the other. One group resembled Rustica. The other closely resembled Paniculata. Plants midway in form between the two—resembling both at once as the original hybrids did—were missing. They had been eliminated. In his experiments East continued to raise the plants of these two groups, without letting them be crossed back with either parent species. The result was that in subsequent generations the plants of the Paniculata group by their own actions became identical with the original Paniculata species, and became fully fertile again, while the plants of the Rustica group in subsequent generations by their own actions became identical with the Rustica species and became fully fertile again (1).

The example of the reversion to species in the case of the rye-wheat cross given above is described by Jones, and at the close of his description he says, "For this reason it is to be expected that wide crosses (i. e. between distinct species) will tend to revert to either parent" (13). The example of the reversion of the Paniculata-Rustica hybrids is described by Professors Babcock and Clausen (1), and at the close of their description of this reversion to species, together with the account of a similar case of reversion in a cross between the two species, emmer and spelt, they say, "In both the hybrids discussed above, there is an illustration of an observation made repeatedly in species hybridization, namely, that the descendants eventually revert to the parental condition." Elsewhere these men also say regarding the phenomenon of reversion in experiments in which common tobacco plants were crossed with other natural species, "This phenomenon of complete return to the parental condition is all the more striking when different varieties of Tabacum (tobacco) are employed in the original hybridization" (1).

In 1914 Luther Burbank, an ardent evolutionist, claimed to have succeeded in making a hybrid between the plum and the apricot, which he called "plum-cot." He boasted at the time that he had broken down a supposed Divine law that distinct species should not permanently be hybridized, and claimed that he had in the "plum-cot" created a permanent new form. The present writer has carefully investigated this case and finds that those who are well acquainted with the hybrid say it is now apparently nothing but a plum. In a letter to the Hon. John M. Nelson, Congressman from Wisconsin, John T. Bregger, successor to Burbank as manager of the "Luther Burbank Experimental Farms," says, "The plum-cot tree looks very much like the plum. The fruit, however, is in color like the plum, but has a short fuzz like an apricot. It is inclined to be somewhat acid in flavor, but very juicy, and some of them very palatable." In a letter to the present writer Prof. W. H. Chandler, head of the Department of Pomology of the University of California says, "All plum-cots that I have seen seem to me to be merely plums." And in another letter Professor Guy L. Philp, Assistant Pomologist at the same university, says, "We have growing here on the station grounds five or six so-called plum-cots. Of this number most of the varieties show no character other than the Japanese plum." When, together with these statements, it is realized that this hybrid, because it is a tree and therefore matures slowly, has had the opportunity to pass through but two or three generations at the most, and reversion to species has not had full opportunity to take place, it can be said that the evidence points strongly to the ultimate reversion of this hybrid, if this has not already taken place.

According to the mass of evidence, permanent hybrids between distinct natural species do not persist. They are unstable and tend to revert. Cases in plant species of what are perhaps actual cases of stable interspecific hybrids have been reported. These abnormal plants are usually kept in greenhouses where, under protected conditions, they are not subject to the rigors and changes of conditions, to which plants in the open are subjected. It is known that certain species of plants can hybridize only when grown very slowly—that is when the temperature is kept cool and the rate of growth of the plant is retarded. Slow growth gives the contrary elements in the hybrid time to adjust themselves to one another. But under rigorous natural conditions where there are sudden changes in temperature and moisture it is more than likely that the interspecific hybrid could not survive. The only hybrids that are permanent unions between different types are those between varieties within species. These should not properly be called hybrids, since the word hybrid implies a violation of nature.

INTERVARIETAL STERILITY DIFFERENT FROM INTERSPECIFIC STERILITY.—Before leaving the discussion of sterility between species, a word should be said about sterility within species, i. e. between varieties. Sterility sometimes exists between members of the same species. This may be due to individual cases of disease. It may be due to a difference in size, e. g. as between a poodle and a mastiff. Certain plants of the same species, e. g. two varieties of the four-o'clock, can not be crossed when one variety of the species is used as the male, because the pollen tubes of that variety are not long enough or not able to grow fast enough to penetrate down to the ovules of the other, but can be crossed when the other variety is the male (16). These causes of intervarietal sterility, however, are purely mechanical or temporary. They are not due to a difference in the germ cells themselves. The germ cells within a species are identical, having the same number, order, and character of chromosomes, and when whatever obstacles to the union of germ cells of organisms within species there may be are removed, the germ cells readily unite to produce a new plant or animal with normal powers of growth and reproduction. The germ cells of distinct species, however, are fundamentally different, and no amount of human ingenuity can remove that difference, so as to enable the germ cells to unite and function normally in the production of a new individual and future generations. Herein lies the great difference between species and varieties in respect of sterility. And to this great difference bear witness the statements of Babcock and Clausen, "A different type of sterility is represented in species hybrid. The sterility of species hybrid is in quite a different category from that of the sterility occurring within species" (1).

OBEDIENCE TO MENDEL'S LAWS ANOTHER IMPORTANT TEST OF SPECIES.—There is another criterion for determining what forms belong to a natural species and what do not. It is a criterion of the very greatest importance and was one totally unknown in the days when Darwin sought to discredit the idea of natural species. The test is based on the facts of Mendelian heredity. It is: Do the generations of offspring of a cross between different forms show strict obedience to Mendel's Laws or not? If they do, the forms are varieties. If they do not, they are distinct species.

As is well known, all the varieties of a species, e.g. all the varieties of the species of fruit-flies, Drosophila Melanogaster, cross-breed readily and follow Mendel's laws of heredity. Within species the various forms are due to certain factors in the germ cells of the members of the species, and these factors segregate and unite according to a definite orderly law. When distinct species are crossed, however, and a few hybrids can be produced which are able to bring forth a few progeny, orderliness disappears and chaos results. The laws of heredity, when two of the same species are crossed and a new individual produced, may be likened to the manner in which a new watch works, which has been made by combining the parts of two watches of exactly the same make. The parts fit perfectly together and work in such harmony that no trouble is experienced. The laws of heredity, when two of different species are crossed, is like the workings of a new watch made by combining the parts of two watches produced by different manufacturers. If the parts can be combined, the watch either will not go at all, or if it goes, does so imperfectly and eventually breaks down. The fault in this illustration, of course, lies in the fact that a watch is made of material which cannot adjust itself when its forms do not fit, whereas a plant or animal is composed of living tissues which are able, within limits, to make adjustments.

The great difference in this respect between varieties and species is described by the well-known evolutionist and student of heredity, Prof. Castle of Harvard, who says, "But in crosses between different species, which do not ordinarily cross under natural conditions, the inheritance is not typically Mendelian, being complicated by blending effect in F_1 (first filial generation), imperfect segregation in F_2 (second filial generation), partial sterility and abnormal sex ratios, things of frequent occurrence in species crosses, as we shall see" (6). And of significance in this same connection is the statement by Babcock and Clausen that crosses between distinct species "exhibit phenomena which do not conform, without marked modifications, to the laws which

167

govern variation and heredity within a species" (1). Consequently we find these last mentioned students of heredity giving a definition of species which marks a definite return to the conception of species held by the old creationists before Darwin's day: "A species, whether wild or domesticated, consists of an assemblage of forms which interbreed freely and produce fertile hybrids conforming to Mendel's laws" (1). They add, "In the majority of instances there is no difficulty in grouping individuals into assemblages of this character."

RETURN TO THE OLD CONCEPTION OF SPECIES.—Through the influence of Darwin, discredit was cast upon the Biblical conception of natural species held by the old scientists, Ray, DeCandolle, Quatrefages and others, and the fact of species was almost entirely ignored in evolutionary discussions. With the rediscovery of Mendelism in 1900, however, the concept of species Darwin had discredited began to come back. In 1913 Bateson, then the leader in the investigation of Mendelian principles of heredity, said, "With the spread of evolutionary ideas, to speak much of the fixity of species has become unfashionable, and yet how striking and inscrutable are the manifestations of that fixity" (3). Again he said, "In the enthusiasm with which evolutionary ideas were received, the specificity of living things was almost forgotten . . . and the scientific world persuaded itself readily that species had, after all, been a mere figment of the human mind. Without presuming to declare what future research only can reveal, I anticipate that, when variation has been properly examined and the several kinds of variability have been successfully distinguished according to their respective natures, the result will render the natural definiteness of species increasingly apparent" (3). In 1914 another voice was raised against the practice of ignoring the existence of natural species. Writing in the *Journal of Heredity* on "The Existence of Natural Species," Dr. O. T. Cook of the Bureau of Plant Breeding, United States Department of Agriculture, said, "That all the plants and animals are organized into species is a fundamental fact of biology . . . The species underlie all . . . Of course these complexities of specific organization and sexuality are very unwelcome ideas to those who are about to solve the problems of evolution and heredity by simple experimental and statistical methods, but no truly biological investigation can disregard the fundamental fact that organisms exist as species" (7). In a paper read in 1926 at a joint discussion of the Botany and Zoology Sections of the British Association for the Advancement of Science on the theme "The Conception of a Species" we find these statements, "A species is a group of individuals of common descent with certain characteristics in common, which are represented in the nucleus of each cell by constant and characteristic sets of chromosomes. Two thousand eight hundred and forty-five species, including all the Phyla, so far examined, show remarkable constancy in their specific sets of chromosomes" (18).

NEW SPECIES NOT ARISING.—Evolutionists talk about the origin of "species"—that is, of the origin of new organisms as a whole. The "origin of species" is considered by them to be their problem. We think their tasks should take another form, namely, to account for the non-miraculous origin not of new, fully equipped and completely functioning individuals, but of the various parts that make up the individual, e. g. lungs, heart, eyes, germ-cells. Even so, evolutionists can not account for the origin of new species, for the reason that, although new varieties of natural species are continually being produced by crossing (see Appendix II), none of these new varieties ever is a new species, separated from its parent forms by a wall of sterility. To be a new species, a variety of a natural species would have to be separated from the species in which it arose by a wall of sterility similar to that which now separates natural species from one another. For example, if a new species were ever to arise out of the dog species, a number of puppies would have to be born that would not be able to cross back with other dogs and yet would be able to cross with each other. Such puppies would then be a new species. This is the way evolutionists say evolution has taken place. The trouble for them is that such puppies or varieties in natural species, either of plants or of animals, are not arising. Now and then some enthusiastic evolutionist reports that such offspring have arisen, but further investigation invariably reveals that the report is erroneous. Bateson said in 1922, "The production of an indubitably sterile hybrid from completely fertile parents, which have arisen under critical observation from a single common origin is the event for which we wait. Until this event is witnessed, our knowledge of evolution is incomplete in a vital respect. From time to time a record of such an observation is published, but none has yet survived criticism" (3). The writer was much interested in a case which seemed partially to fulfill the requirements which Bateson laid down. It was first reported by Prof. H. H. Plough of Amherst College in 1924. A race of fruit-flies was produced by him whose individuals were more fertile *inter se* than with the parent stock. It was hoped by Morgan and others that the sterility toward the parent stock which seemed to have begun in these flies would increase until it was complete. Plough announced that investigation of the case was being continued. In 1929, wishing to learn what had happened to the flies, the writer corresponded with Prof. Plough, who replied in part as follows: "I may say that much of the significance which this case appeared to have for the theory of evolution has probably disappeared, for it has become increasingly clear that the particular stock is not infertile with the wild stock, although it is with many mutant combinations. It has obviously changed in this relation in the past four years—i. e. with selection it has itself become more fertile when inbred, and in so doing seems to have lost its intolerance for the wild (i. e. parent stock) and partially for some others. This is the exact reverse of what one would expect from the situation, and quite destroys its value for the evolutionary theory." Plough's results are typical of all similar cases with other species, and there have been a number which at first looked promising. Returning to England after making the now famous address before the American Association Bateson found himself attacked by his fellow evolutionists for making statements damaging to the cause of evolution. Bateson, however, did not retreat. He said, "I directed once more the attention of naturalists to the fact that we still await the production of indubitably sterile hybrids from completely fertile parents which have arisen under critical observation from a single origin. So far as our knowledge goes, all the domestic races, for example of dogs, of pigeons, of fowls, among animals; and of cabbage, of peas, of Primula Sinensis and many more plants—when inter-crossed among themselves—never produce this sterility in their mongrels, though the races are often distinct enough to pass for species. But if we begin crossing natural species, even those which on our reckoning must be very closely allied, we constantly find either that they will not cross breed, or that if they can be crossed the results are more or less sterile" (3).

The well-known American evolutionist, Morgan, speaking of Bateson's requirements for proof of the origin of new species, says that he questions the necessity of putting the theory of evolution to the test Bateson called for. Such a test, Morgan thinks, would render the demonstration of the origin of species "wellnigh impossible," since it is very unlikely, he thinks, that such a wall of sterility between varieties could arise all at once. Morgan thinks it best to explain the raising up of this wall of sterility between varieties, so as to separate them into distinct species, as the result of the long separation of these varieties, geographically or otherwise. Foxes and dogs, on Morgan's theory, were once simple varieties of one ancient species, just as the fox-terrier and the poodle are now. But dogs and foxes got separated somehow in the ancient days and stayed separated so long that they became the two distinct species which they are today, completely separated by a wall of sterility. Morgan says, "The interpretation of the sterility between species and the sterility of hybrids that seems to me more probable is very different from that suggested by Bateson. Both phenomena, as I interpret them, are the result of many kinds of difference which have arisen in the two species that have been separated for a long time" (14).

Morgan's theory of the origin of new species is pure speculation, and is contrary to whatever evidence bearing on that matter there is. Separation has caused no sterility between varieties of natural species in any known case. Varieties of plants and animals brought from Europe to America soon after its discovery are as perfectly fertile with the European forms when brought back and crossed as they could possibly be. Native domestic cattle of India and of Europe, having been separated for thousands of years, are perfectly fertile today when crossed. In the human species Europeans and American Indians and races of the Far East have no greater difficulty in producing normal

170

children when intermarriage takes place than do those people who live in neighboring villages in the same land, although Europeans, Indians and Polynesians have been separated for thousands of years, living all the while in different climates, engaging in different occupations, eating different foods. Morgan doubtless would say that thousands of years are not long enough for sterility to arise. Millions of years are required. This, however, must be recognized as pure speculation, and is of no interest to one who desires concrete proof of the "origin of species" instead of possibilities which rest on faith. Bateson answered Morgan in advance when he said that "even time can not complete that which has not yet begun" (3).

Reference has already been made (see page 161) to a cross between a cabbage and a radish, which was said to have produced a hybrid plant which grew and grew, but would not produce flowers or seeds. Such was the case for several years. The hybrid could produce no flowers. It was kept alive only by "vegetative reproduction," that is, by cutting off branches from the plant and rooting them. Finally flowers did appear and produced seeds, and when the seeds were planted they brought forth plants like the hybrid itself, and these plants continued to breed true to form. This the evolutionists called "the creation of new species." But it is not the creation of new species in any real sense, for it is nothing but the making of one out of two, or the combination of old material which already existed to form something else. Furthermore, Krapechenko's radish-cabbage hybrid did not persist but reverted or perished, as all other intergeneric hybrids do in time (21) (22).

In 1937 a way was discovered by biologists to cause radish-cabbage hybrids, and other similar hybrids from wide crosses, to reproduce themselves and persist temporarily more quickly than was done in the Russian experiment. This is by the use of a chemical called "colocine," which has the power to cause growing plants to double their ordinary chromosome number. Other chemical agents and artificial ways have been found which will accomplish the same thing, though not as well as with colocine (19). In connection with the discovery of the use of colocine it has been learned what is necessary within a sterile, inter-specific hybrid to make it reproduce itself. That is a doubling of the ordinary chromosome number. This is a condition in reproduction which is artificial—since ordinary reproduction (such as between varieties within species) does not require any such doubling of the chromosomes.

Evolutionists have many unsolved problems which they must explain before they can expect men to give up their faith in creation and in Divine revelation, and not the least of these unsolved problems is the reason why, from purely natural causes, there have come to be what so clearly are natural species, i. e. groups of plants and animals composed of varieties freely interbreeding according to Mendel's Laws and separated by walls of various degrees of sterility from other groups of plants and

171

animals. Darwin sought by "natural selection" to account for the non-miraculous origin of the present world of plants and animals, and he sought by "natural selection" to account for the phenomenon of sterility between species. He was unable to do so. He said, "At one time it appeared to me probable that the sterility of first crosses and of hybrids might have been slowly acquired through natural selection of slightly lessened degrees of fertility . . . After mature reflection, it seems to me that this could not have been effected through natural selection" (8). No evolutionist has been more successful than Darwin in accounting for the sterility which separates species, and no evolutionist has begun to account for the wonderful phenomena of heredity within species known as Mendel's Laws. When Bateson truthfully said in 1922, "That particular and essential bit of the theory of evolution which is concerned with the origin and nature of species remains utterly mysterious" (3), it can be seen what a tremendous task lies ahead of those who wish to supplant the doctrine of special creation with the doctrine of evolution. When the evolutionists have explained "the origin and nature of species" their theory will be worthy of consideration by creationists. Until then creationists will cling to the doctrine of the special creation of each separate species or "kind."

LITERATURE CITED

1. Babcock, E. B., and Clausen, R. E., *Genetics in Relation to Agriculture,* 1927, pages 314; 326; 319; 319-324; 591; 305.

2. Bailey, L. H., and Gilbert, A. W., *Plant Breeding,* 1917, page 111.

3. Bateson, W., *Problems of Genetics,* 1913, pages 16, 21; *Smithsonian Institute Report,* 1915, page 376; *Science,* Jan. 20, 1922; *Nature,* July 15, 1922.

4. Boyd, M., *Journal of Heredity,* Vol. 5, 1914, pages 189-198.

5. Burbank, L., *His Methods and Discoveries,* 1914. Vol. 8, page 11; Vol. 2, pages 63-93; Vol. 4, page 160; Vol. 7, page 63; Vol. 4, page 138; Vol. 2, page 295; Vol. 2, page 275.

6. Castle, W. E., *Genetics and Eugenics,* 1926, page 199.

7. Cook, O. T., *Journal of Heredity,* Vol. 5, 1914, pages 155-8.

8. Darwin, C., *Origin of Species,* 6th ed., page 292.

9. Detlefsen, J. A., *Genetic Studies on Cavy Species Cross,* 1914.

10. De Vries, H., *Plant and Animal Breeding,* 1907, page 1.

11. Gravatt, F. A., *Journal of Heredity,* Vol. 5, 1914, pages 269-272.

12. Hornaday, W. T., *The American Natural History,* 1904, page 103.

13. Jones, D. F., *Selective Fertilization,* 1928, p. 97; *Genetics in Plant and Animal Improvement,* 1925, pages 112; 385; 382; 384; 386-7; 385.

14. Morgan, T. H., *The Genetics of Drosophila,* 1925, page 188; *Evolution and Genetics,* 1925, page 46; 53.

15. Punnett, R., *Mendelism,* 6th ed., 1922, page 182; 183.

16. Sinnott, E. W., and Dunn, L. C., *Principles of Genetics,* 1925, pages 113-114.

17. Wallace, A. R., *Darwinism,* 1890, page 152.

18. Hurst, C. C., *Report for the British Association for the Advancement of Science* (Oxford), 1926, page 356; *Science,* March 18, 1928.

19. Riley, H. P., *Genetics and Cytogenetics,* 1948.

20. Huxley, Julian, *A Modern Synthesis,* 1943.

21. Howard, H. W., *Journal of Genetics,* Vol. 16, 1937.

22. Richharia, R. H., *Journal of Genetics,* Vol. 39, 1937.

Appendix II

"MUTATION"*

Farmers, gardeners, orchardists, animal-breeders and experimenters have long borne witness to the fact that new forms have arisen in the stocks of plants and animals with which they have dealt. It is by the production of these new varieties that man has steadily improved the plants and domestic animals which he values. These new forms have been secured in two ways, either by the purposeful crossing of different varieties, or by discovering them after they had arisen. Luther Burbank, for example, who gave to the world more new and valuable varieties of plants, perhaps, than any other single individual, secured these new varieties either by deliberate crossing of different types and selecting promising new forms that come from the crosses in the second and subsequent generations, or by going about in his fields and picking out new forms that had arisen without any effort on his part. It is in the second manner that some of the most valuable varieties among our plants have been secured. To illustrate, in 1862 a Pennsylvania farmer named Fultz, who had a field of wheat of the kind known as Lancaster Red, observed a number of plants in the field different from the ordinary Lancaster Red. The seeds of these plants he gathered and planted, and found that they bred true, thus producing an excellent new variety known as Fultz Wheat. Again, in 1854 a Virginia farmer named Boughton discovered in his wheat fields a number of plants different from the ordinary. These, being gathered and planted, were the foundation of the variety of wheat called Tappanhannock Wheat. Other valuable varieties of wheat—Gold Coin, Cavalier, Hopetown and others—are said to have come into existence in the same way (2).

In species of plants and animals beside wheat, new forms or varieties are continually arising in a similar manner. Since the discovery of the laws of heredity known as Mendel's Laws, the heredity of plants and animals has been watched very closely, and new forms have been observed to arise in numerous species. A species which has been very closely studied in connection with

*Numbers in parentheses refer to sources of information listed at the end of the appendix. The word factor is used for gene.

Mendel's Laws is the fruit-fly, Drosophila Melanogaster, under the leadership of Prof. T. H. Morgan of Columbia University, and in this species under human observation considerable numbers of forms different from the normal have arisen. "Mutations," "mutants," "sports," "saltations" are names that are commonly given to these new forms, and they are said by evolutionists to be spontaneous, new additions to the organic world, new "creations," the "materials with which the evolution process builds."

These new forms can not be truly new additions to the world of organisms if the Bible record of creation is true, since "on the seventh day God finished the work which He had made," and nothing genuinely new has come into being since. It is the purpose of this discussion, therefore, to show from nature itself that it is not necessary at all to believe that any new form which arises today under human observation or otherwise is truly new, but that it may be and very likely is creation old, having been placed in the species in the creative days and been hidden or latent in the species until somehow it has been revealed to man.

Description of Mutations.—All so-called mutations appear suddenly. Before the observer is aware of their presence they are there. They are changes from what seems to be the normal form of the species, changes affecting one or several different parts of the organism at once. Among the mutations which have appeared at separate times in the normally red eyed fruit-fly, Drosophila, are eyes of over thirty different colors, such as cherry, scarlet, blood, apricot, purple, buff, coral, vermilion, ecru, eosin, mahogany, ivory, rose, pink, white (12). New forms have also arisen in this species by changes not only in color, but in the size and shape of the body, wings, legs, and hairs of the flies. (See Fig. 56.) Once having appeared, all mutations are found to be obedient to Mendel's Laws in the same manner that forms or characters said to be old are. The vast majority of mutations behave in heredity as simple recessives. Of the several hundred mutants which have appeared in the fruit-fly, only about ten behave as dominants. Once having arisen, mutations usually breed perfectly true. In some cases the so-called mutant form goes back again to the normal, wild form from which it sprang. For example, in flies which have been closely watched, red (normal) eyed flies have given rise to white-eyed flies; these white-eyed flies have given rise to eosin (pinkish yellow) eyed flies; these eosin eyed flies have given rise to red (normal) eyed flies; and these red (normal) eyed flies have given rise to white eyed flies (12). One special feature which is supposed to distinguish a "mutation" from a simple variation is that a mutation is a form that appears seldom, while a variation is a form that appears often. This, however, is not a proper distinction, as we shall see. It is significant that a new form is called a mutation as long as the exact manner of its production is not understood. When, however, the Mendelian Law by which a new form arises is discovered and men know that they can themselves produce it

175

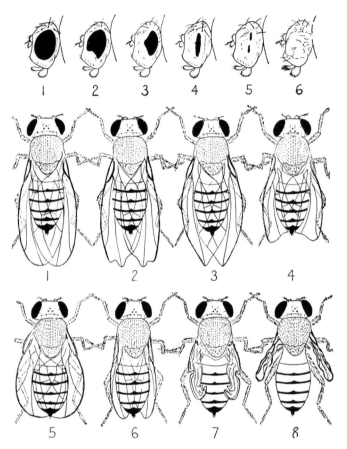

Fig. 56. A few of several hundred "new" forms of the fruit-fly *Drosophila Melanogaster*, which have arisen since 1910 from the so-called wild type of this species. At the top is a row of heads showing from the side various forms of eyes which have arisen. No. 1 is the normal eye possessed by the wild type fly. Nos. 2-6 are mutant forms, true breeding, called respectively *kidney, lobe, bar, ultra-bar, no-eye*. Below are drawings of flies showing new mutant types of wings. No. 1 is the form of wing of the wild type fly. Nos. 2-8 are mutant forms called respectively *notch, cut, truncate, broad, miniature, club, vestigial.* The wild fly has four pairs of chromosomes, and all the "new" forms which have arisen have also four chromosomes. The "new" forms are all fertile with one another and with the parent form, but not fertile with any other species of fly. Note that the mutations are losses rather than gains in structure. All our breeds of domestic animals have doubtless come by "mutation" just as have these new forms of flies.

by breeding, it is no longer called a "mutation" but a variation of old material.

WHAT A MUTATION IS ACCORDING TO EVOLUTIONARY DOCTRINE.—A mutation is said by evolutionists to be the spontaneous origination in the germ cells of species of new genes which did not exist before. A mutation in the evolutionary sense is a new creation, something coming out of nothing, or at least something greater coming out of something less.

WHAT A MUTATION IS ACCORDING TO THE CREATION VIEW.—A mutation is believed by those who uphold the Biblical doctrine of creation to be but the revealing of hidden genes put into species by the Creator in an act of special creation.

IGNORANCE OF THE ORIGIN OF TRULY NEW FORMS BY "MUTATION" ON THE PART OF EVOLUTIONISTS.—Those who would have us believe that mutations are something genuinely new added to the world by some mysterious, creative process to be building blocks for evolution can give no explanation whatever of what causes these new forms thus to arise. While it is understood, and may readily be granted, that the changes which produce mutation phenomena have their basis in the germ cells of the species, devotees of evolution walk in confessed ignorance of what produces them there. The changes producing mutations are described by Prof Conklin of Princeton as being "sudden transformations in Mendelian factors themselves, comparable to changes in chemical composition," but what brings about these alchemistic-like "transformations" this evolutionist is unable to say. He can only say, "The cause of new hereditary characters, or rather mutations in genes (factors), is obscure" (5). Other evolutionists have likewise acknowledged their ignorance of how these new "creations" arise by mutation. Professors Sinnott and Dunn of the University of Connecticut say, "the cause and origin of which (mutations) we do not understand" (14). Professors Babcock and Clausen of the University of California say, "Concerning the causes of mutations nothing is known" (1). Professors Bailey and Gilbert of Cornell University say, "What do new characters come from? The answer to this question would give us the keynote to the whole situation" (2). Professor H. S. Jennings of Johns Hopkins University says, "We do not understand the causes of these changes (mutations).; we do not know how they are produced" (9). Professor H. H. Newman of Chicago University says, "In bringing this discussion of the causes of heritable variations (mutations) to a close, we find ourselves in a somewhat pessimistic frame of mind. When all is said, it is found that our knowledge of what actually causes mutations is almost nothing. The really great evolutionary discovery of the future will probably be the finding out of the cause or the causes of mutations" (13).

WHY EVOLUTIONISTS MAINTAIN MUTATIONS ARE NEW.—The question naturally arises at this point, "Why then, in view of such acknowledged ignorance, do evolutionists insist that mutations

177

are really new creations?" It is best to let one of their number, Professor Gates of London University, answer that question, which he does in his book *Mutations and Evolution.* He says, "To attempt to explain mutations away by assuming that nothing new has really appeared is tantamount to a denial of evolution" (7). In other words, if mutations are not the coming into being of something really new there is and has been no evolution. The reason which this evolutionist gives is perfectly sufficient for some people, so prejudiced are they in favor of the evolutionary theory. Needless to say, however, it is not a reason that can satisfy those who do not believe in evolution or are seeking the truth in the matter.

EXPLANATION OF MUTATIONS [1] SIMPLE DOMINANCE.—Mutations as the revelations of old, hidden forms through crossing have various simple explanations, and one of the simplest has its basis in the Mendelian Law of dominance. Investigation has disclosed that an old, recessive factor which is introduced into a strain of plants or a breed of animals in the beginning, may be concealed for an indefinite number of generations and be brought to light again whenever two individuals, each containing the recessive factor, are mated. How this can be will now be pointed out.

If an albino guinea pig is mated with a pure-breeding (homozygous) black guinea pig, the white character will disappear in the first generation of offspring, since black is dominant and white is recessive. If a male and female of this first, impure-breeding (heterozygous or hybrid) generation are mated, the albino character will reappear in the second filial generation in the proportion of one albino to three black guinea pigs (Fig 30). Thus, for one generation the white character will be concealed and then again revealed. If, however, one of the first, impure (heterozygous) generation of black guinea pigs is crossed with a pure (homozygous) black guinea pig, all of the offspring will still be black. The albino character will not be able to appear, and thus, for two generations, this visible character will be hid. And as long as a pure-breeding (homozygous) black guinea pig is one of the two engaged in the cross, be it male or female, the white character must continue to be hidden. Not until an impure-breeding (heterozygous) black guinea pig is permitted to mate with another impure black animal can the white character again come forth, when it will do so in the ratio three to one. What has been described here as taking place under the control of men can also take place under the control of nature, and thus a very old form, one introduced into the stock at the very beginning (at creation), can be brought to light as an apparently new thing.

One of the characteristics that causes new forms to be called "mutations" is that they appear at very infrequent intervals. It is easy, however, to understand how it could come about in nature that a recessive character should be enabled to appear extremely seldom. If the reader will turn to Figure 30 and imagine, first, that the number of generations presented there, both of the pure (homozygous) and the impure (heterozygous) lines, were increased until a million guinea pigs were in existence; second, would then imagine that every white guinea pig was killed; third, would then imagine that the black guinea pigs surviving were left to run wild and cross-breed among themselves promiscuously, a white guinea-pig could appear among the blacks only when two impure-breeding (heterozygous) black animals (i. e. such as are in the middle column) happened to mate. This, as the reader can see, would, on the basis of chance, all other things being equal as in this case, be very seldom. Such occasional white guinea pigs, when they did appear, would then be true "mutations" in character.

The Galloway is a black breed of cattle. Very rarely, however, breeders of Galloway cattle are disappointed to find that a red calf has been born. The reason for this phenomenon is described by Babcock and Clausen as follows, "Since red is a simple recessive to black, and since red animals occurred in a foundation stock of the breeds at no very remote time, their appearance is presumably due to chance mating between two animals which were heterozygous for red and probably traced back through an unbroken line of heterozygous ancestors to the foundation stock of the breed" (1). The above mentioned professors have made a calculation that if a breeder started with two black cattle which he had secured by mating a dominant black with a recessive red, and which were therefore both heterozygous for red and black (i. e. having genes for both red and black in their germ-cells), and proceeded out of these two to build up a great herd of black cattle by killing off every red animal that was born, in two hundred generations only one per cent of the black cattle would be heterozygous, having genes for red (1). In a vast herd of black cattle thus produced, say ten thousand head, a red calf might at rare intervals be born. Such a red calf would then have all the ear-marks of a "mutation," provided that no man had ever before seen a red calf and did not know that a red factor had been introduced into the herd in the very beginning. Evolutionists once considered the appearance of off-colored, recessive forms in pure domestic breeds of cattle as genuine mutations. Of late they have been compelled to back down from that position. We quote Sinnott and Dunn: "Occasionally, for instance, a red and a white calf appears in a pure-bred herd of black and white Holstein cattle in which only black and white animals have been recorded for several generations. Cole has found that red in such cases is not a new trait, but one which may have been present in the stock for many generations. Being recessive, the factor for red may be carried but not expressed until the chance mating of two heterozygotes provides the opportunity" (14).

Color mutations of the kind described above are among the most common and most characteristic mutations, and they are occasionally appearing in many wild species. In grey field mice and in wild rats, pure white animals very rarely appear. In

179

skunks an albino animal has been known to occur once in a long while. The same is true in coyotes. How we shall look at these so-called mutations is the question. Shall we consider them as the appearing of old, concealed factors for white color of coats in those species, or shall we consider them as the evolutionists would have us do, as the coming of something truly new into the world? In view of what is known to be possible in the building up of a herd of cattle, and of what actually takes place in the reappearance of red calves in black breeds, it is more than likely that these so-called mutations in skunks and field mice and coyotes and other species are simply due to the fact that there are in those species comparatively few individuals who are heterozygous (i. e. carrying the factor for white in their germs), and it is only very seldom that two of such heterozygous individuals chance to mate. When they do white animals are produced. It is easy to see why so few of such heterozygous individuals should exist in the species mentioned. For one thing, such white varieties of the species are more conspicuous to their enemies than their fellows of a more dark and sober color, and the white forms, when they have appeared, have not been often able to survive long in the particular environments in which they appeared. They have, therefore, been selected out by nature just as the breeder selects out the red in a herd of black cattle he is building up. Figure 38 illustrates the concealment of the single-comb character (a recessive) for many generations in the manner described above. In this diagram the single-comb character might have been brought out at any point along the line by the mating of two hybrid (heterozygous) rose-comb chickens. The manner in which it is brought out in the diagram merely illustrates a special feature of Mendelian heredity in fowls. See Punnett's *Mendelism,* 6th ed., page 30.

We have discussed one of the simplest manners in which apparently new forms may arise through cross breeding or hybridization by the use of old material, and doubtless this is one of the most common ways. There are, however, other possible ways in which crossing may bring forth old forms new to man. Mendelian investigation has revealed a great complexity in the laws of heredity discovered by Mendel. Many modifications of the fundamental laws first discovered have been revealed. These modifications in no way destroy or weaken the general principles of Mendel's discovery. On the contrary they strengthen those principles. The discussion in this appendix does not pretend to be an exposition of the several modifications of Mendel's Laws, but a number of such modifications will be briefly described in order to give some conception of the many different ways it is possible for very old forms to be concealed in species and then be revealed through chance mating.

EXPLANATIONS OF MUTATIONS [2] COMPLEMENTARY FACTORS.—
Most of the outward characters men see in plants and animals are due to the effect of but one factor acting alone. It may in

future be discovered by students of heredity that all visible characters are due to the combined effect of many factors instead of one, which at present seems to be the case. It is already known, however, that some visible characters can arise only when two or more factors are present. Bateson and Punnett found that in sweet peas, for example, there are white sweet peas which, when crossed with some white sweet peas, produced only white flowers, but which, when mated with other white sweet peas produce only purple flowers. Investigation of this phenomenon disclosed that in each of the white sweet peas which, by crossing, produced purple flowers, there were two independent factors. Separately each of these two independent factors produce white flowers. Together they produce only colored flowers. By chance two of the right kind of white flowers were mated by Bateson and Punnett, and that mating brought together the two factors which together produce colored flowers. The first appearance of those colored sweet peas among white sweet peas was of the exact character of a mutation—the sudden, unexpected appearance of something apparently new. The colored flowers, however, were not truly new, for they were exactly like the wild, purple sweet peas that have been growing in Sicily for centuries (14). (See Fig. 57.)

In the above case two factors coming together are necessary to produce a striking change similar in character to a mutation. Cases are known, however, when more than two factors are necessary to produce a new form. Purple corn is an odd type of corn that was being raised by the Indians of America when it was discovered. Purple corn, it has been learned, can not be produced in non-purple strains of corn unless four independent factors are brought together. With any one of these four independent factors missing purple corn is not produced (10).

Let the reader at this point pause and consider what this means in regard to producing very rare, yet very old forms by cross breeding. Let him assume, for example, that in a natural species, e. g. fruit-flies, four factors coming together in one individual would produce a white-eyed fly. In order for the white-eyed form to appear two flies would have to mate, one having two of the necessary factors and the other having two, or one having three of the necessary factors and the other having one. Either way the four necessary factors would be brought together and the white-eyed flies would appear. The event might not be a rare one if many or most of the interbreeding flies carried one, two or three of the necessary factors. If, however, many of the flies carried none of the necessary factors, or only one, it would be a rare event indeed when the four required factors got together. But when they did, lo, a mutation. The situation can be partially visualized by reference to the game of cards. Those who are familiar with card games know how seldom four of the same kind all fall together in one hand when four people are playing. When eight are playing it is still more seldom. Yet it sometimes happens. This chance coming together of certain cards

181

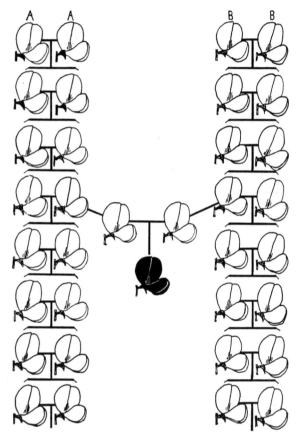

Fig. 57. Illustration of "mutation" produced by complementary factors. The column of flowers at the left, marked AA, represents one strain of white sweet peas. That at the right, marked BB, represents another strain. The two strains are white because of the presence in them of two genes for whiteness that are distinct from one another but which produce exactly the same effect. Separate from one another these genes produce only white flowers, but when they come together in one individual they have the combined effect of producing colored flowers. Designing the gene for white in the left column as A, and the gene for white in the other column as B, in Mendelian terminology it is said that AA produces white flowers; BB produces white flowers; AB produces colored flowers.

illustrates the chance getting together of multiple factors necessary for the production of new forms. Four seems to be a large
number of factors necessary to produce a specific visible character, yet it is said by Mendelian investigators that cases are
known in which some visible characters are produced only when
there are as many as seven, twelve, and even more factors present
together (14).

EXPLANATION OF MUTATIONS [3] INHIBITING FACTORS.—Of
a somewhat similar nature to the cases cited, though not exactly the same, are those cases in which a visible character which
might be called a mutation can appear only when one factor is
removed. There are known to be cases when certain old forms
latent or hidden in plants and animals are prevented from appearing as long as two independent factors are together, but when,
by chance mating, these two independent factors are separated, the
forms come out. As an example may be taken the case of the
chickens called White Leghorns. White Leghorns produce only
white chicks when White Leghorns are bred among themselves.
But when a White Leghorn is mated with a White Wyandotte, a
few, but a very definite proportion of colored offspring appear
in the descendants. Investigation of this hereditary phenomenon
has revealed that White Leghorns are white because of the presence of two independent factors acting together. White Leghorns
are really colored chickens, having the color prevented from appearing by a factor which is called an "inhibitor." This inhibiting
factor does nothing but inhibit or prevent the color factor from
showing its effect. When, however, this inhibiting factor gets
separated from the color factor, as it does in some of the second
filial generation when White Leghorns and White Wyandottes are
crossed, the color factor shows its effect and colored chickens
are produced (14). (See Fig. 58.) No cases are yet known when
a certain visible character in a species is inhibited by more than
one inhibiting factor. Such cases may be found to exist. But
enough is already known to suggest how a rare and apparently
new form, a "mutation," may be for ages concealed in a species
and only be revealed when by a chance crossing of two varieties
the factor inhibiting the form is removed. The removing of inhibiting factors is one very likely way in which dominant mutations
are revealed.

EXPLANATIONS OF MUTATIONS [4] DUPLICATE FACTORS.—A
number of cases are known where there are several independent
factors, each of which separately produces the same effect, and
each of which is dominant to one and the same kind of recessive
factor. In corn, for example, it has been discovered that there is
a factor we will call A, which produces yellow color in the kernels
This factor A is dominant over a recessive factor which makes
the kernels white. But it has also been discovered that there is
another factor in corn, which we will call B, which also produces yellow color in the kernels, and this factor B is also

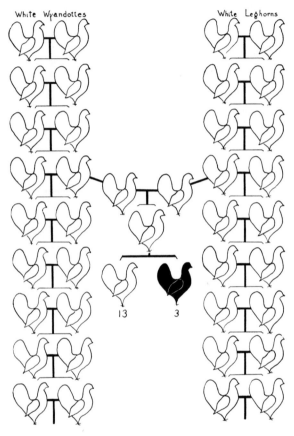

Fig. 58. Illustration of "mutation" produced by inhibiting factors. The column at the left represents a pure breed of White Wyandotte poultry. These chickens are white because of a simple factor for whiteness in them. The column at the right represents a pure breed of White Leghorns. These chickens are white exactly like the Wyandottes but for an entirely different reason. White Leghorns have a factor in them which would make them colored were it not for the fact that there is also in them a factor called an "inhibitor" which prevents the color from showing. All colored breeds of Leghorn chickens, of which there are several, have not this inhibiting factor which makes White Leghorns white. Whenever a White Wyandotte and a White Leghorn are crossed there is a separation of the inhibiting and the color factors in three out of every sixteen second-generation offspring, and the color comes out that number of times

dominant over a factor which produces white. Here, therefore, we have two independent, dominant factors which produce yellow corn, whether they are both present together or whether only one is present. In this case it makes no difference in the visible effect whether one factor for yellow or both factors produce the color. The yellow is just the same, and the white can not appear. If, now, any corn-plant having the single factor for yellow, A, is crossed with a plant having a white factor, all the offspring will be yellow, and if two of these offspring are then mated the white color will again reappear in one out of every four progeny. The same will be true if a plant with the single factor for yellow, B, is crossed with a plant having a factor for white. The first generation of offspring of this cross likewise will be yellow and two of these offspring, if crossed, will produce but one white out of every four progeny. It sometimes happens in corn that both factors for yellow color of kernels, A and B, are together in one plant. When such a plant is crossed with a plant having factors for white, only yellow-kerneled offspring are produced in the first generation. But, when two of the first generation are mated, white kerneled offspring appear only in the proportion of one out of every sixteen, which would give it the character of a mutation, since one of the characteristics of new forms which causes men to call them mutations is that they appear seldom. The reader may learn how this is but a simple outworking of Mendel's Law if he will turn to Figure 35 of this book. There he will find in the second filial generation (bottom row) sixteen guinea pigs in all (9 plus 3 plus 3 plus 1 equals 16). If, now, he will imagine that those are corns instead of guinea pigs, and will substitute in that figure the word "yellow" for the word "short" every place "short" appears, and will substitute the word "yellow" for the word "colored" every place "colored" appears, and will substitute the word "white" for the words "long" and "uncolored" every place those words appear, he will, by bearing in mind that yellow dominates white, see how simply the proportion fifteen to one arises. It would make no difference whether the two dominant factors for yellow were both in one of the original parents and the two recessive factors for white in the other, or whether one factor for yellow were in each parent and one factor for white in each. In the first and subsequent generations the color results would be the same. The first generation would all be yellow, and the second generation be white once in every sixteen offspring. The significance of the fact that a yellow factor might be in each of the original parents is that the presence of the white factor in the stock would thus be concealed and perhaps unknown, and when it was revealed it would seem to be something new.

In the case described above, there are two independent, dominant factors for the same thing and two independent recessives for the same thing. There is known another case, however, where there are three independent, dominant factors for the same thing and all three dominant to one kind of recessive form. This is the case of wheat (15). It has been found in wheat that there are three independent factors for red color of seeds, all of which are dominant to the same kind of white factor. In such a case recessive white seeds could appear in the second generation of offspring under certain conditions only in one out of every sixty-four. Figure 36 can be made use of in understanding this result.

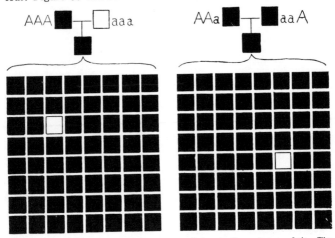

Fig. 59. Illustration of "mutation" produced by duplicate factors. *Left.* The two squares at the top represent two parents (male and female) having three pairs of genes in which three similar dominant genes *AAA,* dominate three similar recessives, *aaa.* In the male are all the dominant genes, in the female all the recessives. From a mating of these parents only offspring showing the dominant trait will appear in the first generation. But from an intermating of these offspring an average of one offspring showing the recessive trait will appear in every sixty-four in the second generation. *Right.* The two squares again represent two parents having in them the same three pairs of genes. But in this case the male has only two of the dominant genes, *AA,* with one recessive, *a,* and the female has only two recessive genes, *aa,* with one dominant, *A,* the result being that male and female parents look alike. Yet the same results will follow in the first and second generation of offspring as when the original male parent carried all the dominant, and the female all the recessive factors. Since the existence of no recessive trait was to be seen in the original parents, its appearance in one of every sixty-four second generation offspring would seem to be the coming forth of some new thing.

Such white-seeded plants, when they appeared, would be of the nature of mutations. They would appear unexpectedly and very seldom, and would seem to be new. Yet they would be old, held in concealment by three factors, any one of which alone is able to conceal it.[155] (See also Fig. 59.)

155 The case of wheat here described differs from the case of corn described above in that the redness of the wheat seeds differs according to the number of factors present. If one factor for red is present there is a certain depth of redness. If two factors for red are present there is a deeper redness, and if three are present a still deeper redness. The principle, however, remains the same.

No actual cases have yet been discovered in any species where there are more than three factors for the same thing, all dominant to one recessive factor. However, it would not be surprising if such should be discovered. Mendelian students have only begun to scratch the surface of the heredity of each individual plant and animal species. It is not at all unlikely that six, eight, and even ten duplicate factors, such as have been described above, exist in some species, and each of these factors is capable of dominating and concealing one and the same old, recessive form. It has been calculated on the basis of Mendel's Law that if there were four duplicate factors in a species and but one kind of recessive to them all, that recessive could appear but once in 256 times. Figure 37 can be used for the understanding of this result. It has been calculated that if there were five duplicate factors and but one kind of recessive, the recessive could appear but once in 1,024 times; that if there were six duplicate factors and one recessive, that recessive could appear but once in 4,096 times; if seven duplicate factors, once in 16,384 times; if eight, once in 65,536 times; if ten, once in 16,777,216 times. Surely, if a form should arise but once in 16,777,216 individuals, men would think they were justified in saying that a truly new form had arisen. Yet it would not necessarily be new at all. It is well to quote here one of the leading students of Mendelism, who has come to realize that no matter how seldom a variety may appear it is not necessarily new. Professor Jones of Yale says, "On account of the great complexity which can easily occur in Mendelian phenomenon, it must be emphasized strongly that the numbers in which new forms appear, however, few they may be, is no proof that they are mutations." (10). Prof. Lotsy, the Dutch botanist, says, "Knowing how difficult it is to show that a given form is free from recessives, we must disqualify, *a priori,* all claims of having proved the existence of mutations based on the demonstration that a certain form has thrown recessives no matter in how feeble proportions" (11).

EXPLANATION OF MUTATIONS [5] LINKAGE.—Thus far we have considered mutation phenomena which have had their basis entirely in the actions of the factors (genes) themselves. There is, however, another highly important and very likely cause of mutation phenomena, one which has its basis in the way factors are often combined with one another in heredity. This is called "linkage." It has been discovered that some factors do not behave like free and independent units, each one able to go its own way always, independent of all other factors. Some factors behave as if they were tied or linked together with another factor and are limited in their freedom by what that other factor does. In the fruit-fly, for instance, there is a factor which produces black color in the fly, and another factor which produces "vestigial" shape of wings. These two factors, one for black and the other for "vestigial" wings, always tend to stay together in heredity, so that a fly that is black also usually has vestigial wings (12). Again, in the same

187

species, there is a factor which produces white eyes, and also a factor which produces yellow body color. These two factors always tend to stay together in heredity, so that a fly with white eyes has also usually a yellow body. Sometimes, however, these factors which are linked together, separate. The tie is broken, and the fly with white eyes is produced without having a yellow body. In the case of some species which have been very closely studied the exact percentage of times when the linkage between certain associated factors is broken, or when there is a "cross-over" as it is called, has been learned. The percentage is very regular and evidently follows a definite law.[156]

Thus far in our discussion of "linkage" little has been disclosed to the reader which can explain mutations. This, however, will appear when it is realized that sometimes in species factors for certain visible characters are linked with inhibiting or lethal factors. A lethal factor is one whose effect is to prevent the individual into which it comes from being formed, or of killing it immediately when it is formed. In the fruit-fly they are known to be exceedingly numerous. Let the reader at this point consider what opportunity a factor for a certain visible character which was tied up with a lethal factor would ever have of expressing itself. It could never express itself as long as it was linked with the lethal, for the reason that the lethal would prevent the organism from being born. As a concrete example let us take the white-eye mutation in fruit-flies. Imagine that the factor which produces white eyes in this species is closely linked with a lethal factor. Like Mary's lamb, wherever that factor for white-eyes goes, the lethal factor is also sure to go. What is the result? White-eyed flies never appear, because the lethal that goes with it prevents every white-eyed fly from being born. When, however, might white-eyed flies appear? Answer—whenever the linkage between the factor for white eyes and the lethal factor connected with it is broken and the factor for white eyes comes into an offspring alone. (Fig. 60.)

We have in this modification of Mendel's Law known as "linkage" and "cross-over," as we have already said, one of the most important, if not the chief of all the possible explanations of the rare appearance of apparently new forms. Some mutations appear more often, some less. A simple and satisfactory explanation is that, as is known to be the case, some of these visible forms are very closely tied up with lethal factors and the linkage between the factors producing those visible forms and the lethal factors is seldom broken. Sometimes, however, the tie is broken. "Crossing over" takes place in a chromosome in the right spot, and the visible form is enabled to appear as a new character. The very great importance of linkage as an explanation of mutations is apparent from the following statements. Conklin says, "If recessive factors are linked with a lethal they can not come to expres-

156 Any late book on genetics will explain the germinal mechanism underlying the phenomenon of "linkage" and "cross-overs."

sion, for recessives appear only when mated with other recessives. But if 'crossing over' should take place in such a way as to break the linkage between the lethal and the recessive factors, the latter would, when homozygous, come to expression as ordinary Mendelian recessives" (5). Jones says, "By a crossing-over a lethal factor may be gotten out of one chromosome, and a few pure-breeding individuals may appear. In this way new types may be brought to light, the occurrence of which is similar in every way

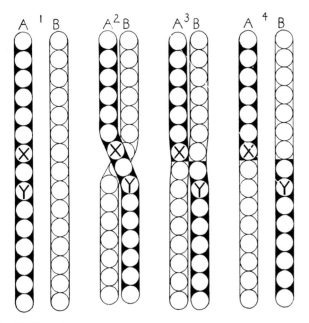

Fig. 60. Illustration of a "mutation" produced by a cross-over. Number 1 above stands between a single pair of mated chromosomes, one of which, the black (marked A) came from the father, the other of which, the white (marked B) came from the mother. Each of these chromosomes is passed on to the offspring either whole or with parts interchanged. (See No. 4.) The white circles represent genes or factors, which are located on the chromosomes arranged in a series from one end to the other. A single chromosome may have thousands of these factors, for they are exceedingly small. The white circles marked X and Y are two factors close together. Circle X represents a factor for producing some visible character which man has never seen. That factor was put there by the Creator. Circle Y represents a lethal factor of some other kind, which, by its close association with X, prevents X from visible manifestation as long as chromosome A remains intact. When, however, as may happen in germ-cell formation X and Y becomes separated by a crossing over (See No. 2, 3, 4) and the factors X and Y go into different germ cells, factor X is able to manifest itself in the individual that it goes into. Thus an apparently new form of the species appears to man, although the factor which produced it was creation old.

to the manner in which many mutations in the organism are found to occur" (10). So important are cross-overs as a means of explaining "mutations" that geneticists have wondered whether "all mutations may not be due to crossing over" (12). It is certainly true that it may offer the explanation of a vast number of them.

EXPLANATION OF MUTATIONS [6] PHYSICAL OR CHEMICAL VARIATIONS IN GENE STRUCTURE. The genes (factors) in the chromosomes, being physical things, must have some molecular shape. What the shape of any gene is no one knows. Different genes may have different shapes. But it may be that a gene is of such a shape or of such chemistry that it can be turned over or about in its place in such a way as to lie in different positions at different times, and it may be that each new position produces a different visible effect in the adult organism. A gene may be imagined like a child's toy-block, a thing which may lie on any one of six sides. Each different position, in the case of a gene, may produce a different result. To mention a definite case, there is a series of eleven eye-colors in the fruit-fly, that is to say, there are eleven eye-color changes which have occurred, which seem to be due to changes in a single gene located in one spot in the first chromosome, the spot being called the "white-locus." These color-changes range from deep red to pure white. They are red, coral, blood, cherry, eosin, apricot, ivory, tinge, buff, ecru, white. The appearance of these eleven different eye colors at different times can be explained as due to a single gene which produces different colors in the eye depending on the position in which the gene lies. If this gene is shaped like a polygon having eleven sides, each side being able to produce a different effect as the polygon is turned, we have an analogy that can explain very well the changes in eye color that have occurred in the fruit-fly from changes known to be at the white locus. Something causes the gene there to turn over, and when it does a new color appears. It can readily be seen, however, that the causing of mutations by the turning about of a gene is not adding something new to the world any more than it is adding something new if a toy is turned about in different ways. That the above is another possible explanation of mutations is borne out by the statement of Morgan. "There is also another fact that the study of the mutation process has brought to our attention. The same mutation may occur again and again. A list of these recurrent mutations is given elsewhere. The appearance of the same mutant indicates that we are dealing with a specific and orderly process. Its recurrence recalls Galton's famous analogy of the polygon. Each change corresponds to a new stable position (perhaps in a chemical sense) of the gene. Tempting as is the comparison, we must remember that, as yet, we have almost no evidence as to the real nature of the mutation process" (12).

Something must also be said about the very remarkable production of mutations by the use of X-rays and radium rays. Under the leadership of H. J. Miller of Texas University fruit-flies and other species of animals and plants have been subjected to these rays, and mutation phenomena have been produced with a far greater frequency than under normal conditions. Exactly what causes the mutations to occur under these rays is not certainly known. It is known that the rays break up the chromosomes, and this breaking up of the chromosomes may release genes for visible characters from lethal connections. The altering of the genes in the manner described in the preceding paragraph is another thing that may occur. But whatever be the explanation of the effect of X-ray and radium rays, the mutations produced by them are not essentially different from those that occur less frequently under normal conditions. In fruit-flies old mutant forms long familiar are produced under X-raying over and over again. A few new mutant forms have been produced, but these may also occur under natural conditions. Prof. M. Drummond of Glasgow University has said, "Miller has shown that when eggs of normal specimens of Drosophila are subjected to X-ray radiation, they give rise to 'mutations' of the same kind as some of those which turn up in Morgan's cultures." Miller himself has said the same thing.

It is obvious from the foregoing that there is no necessity on the basis of the evidence for saying any mutant form is "new" in the strict sense of that word. Some very prominent authorities among evolutionists see this and admit it. Jones says, "As used, the term mutation is given to heritable variations which occur in such a way that no clear reason for their appearance is known. More and more characters, once considered mutations, are now known to be the results of a normal working of a definite mechanism. All mutations may ultimately be understood as the result of an orderly process" (10).

What one leading evolutionist has had to say about mutations being truly new additions to the world should be told. This is Dr. J. P. Lotsy, of the University of Leyden (also director of the Holland Government Herbarium, and Secretary of the International Association of Botanists). So convinced was Lotsy that the revealing of hidden forms by crossing and not the origination of genuinely new forms by a mysterious, creative process is the cause of mutation phenomena, that he put his ideas into a book called *Evolution by Means of Hybridization*. One of the chief things Lotsy does in his book is to show that those who argue that mutations are something genuinely new do not show that the conditions are fulfilled which would prove without a doubt that mutations are the production of new things. To establish clearly that a genuinely new form had come into the world by "mutation," Lotsy says that it would be necessary to show without any question that the race or stock out of which an apparently new form came did not contain that form previously in a hidden condition. The analogy Lotsy uses is a good one. He said a man might claim that he had gotten silver out of nickel by a change in the element nickel, and would prove it by showing the silver. His proof, Lotsy said, would be lacking in certainty until the man

191

had first proved that the nickel was pure and absolutely did not contain any silver to begin with. This, Lotsy says, is what those who claim mutations are genuinely new things fail to do. They fail to show that the stocks or races out of which new forms came did not contain them already. He says, "Mendelism could show us that such a mutation (i. e. something new added) had taken place if we were sure—it is the old difficulty again—of the specific purity of the material from which the supposed mutants arose. Does the classic subject of mutation, Oenothera Lamarckiana (Evening Primrose) give us proof of the existence of such mutations? The answer is an unconditional: "No" (11). He then goes on to say that getting "mutants" out of the Evening Primrose, on which the theory of evolution by mutation was first based by de Vries, is "comparable to the bringing to light the presence of silver in a lead-ore containing silver." In other words, every mutant form from the Evening Primrose was already present in the species. Lotsy then further states that he can not accept any case of reported mutation as a genuine case because in no such case has it been proved satisfactorily that the stock from which the new form rose was pure to start with. After specifying a certain test for purity which any breed of animals or strain of plants must be able to stand before a new form can truly be said to have arisen from it by mutation, Lotsy says, "As far as I am aware, no pretended case of mutation can stand this test" (11). Perfect purity is an absolute essential in the proof that a genuine mutation has occurred, and in no case where a mutation has occurred has perfect purity beforehand been established.

Old forms being brought out by crossing is the simplest explanation of all mutation phenomena. Evolutionists as a whole, however, refuse to accept it. The reason has already been suggested. Such an explanation is a denial of evolution. This is acknowledged by Conklin when he says, "Lotsy maintains that all mutations arise in this way (by crossing). But such an explanation does not account for the existence of the original 'elementary species,' and if they be referred to still earlier crossings it is evident that we only put off the explanation to a more remote period" (5). Of like tenor are the words of Professor Coulter of Chicago University. He says, " 'Evolution through hybridization' is a theory that was suggested by Weismann some decades ago, and has recently been developed and championed by Lotsy . . . While there is little question that natural hybridization takes place and may be a real factor in producing new varieties, at the same time this theory is not satisfactory as a 'complete' explanation of evolution. It seems rather obvious that, although hybridization can multiply variations through crossing forms that are already different from each other, it can never account for the 'original' differences" (6). And clearest of all are the words of Castle, "Some refer all multiplicity of varieties to past hybridization of species genetically different, but this is only referring to a more remote period the genetic changes which are involved in the origin of the hypothetical species themselves. The genetic changes must have occurred *sometime* if related species really had a common orgin as we, under the Darwinian theory, suppose" (4) :[157] One evolutionist, Gates, complainingly calls the explanation of new forms by crossing a "bogey"(7).

Evolutionists can not prove by science that any mutant form is a genuinely new "creation," nor can believers in the Bible prove that any particular form is creation old. Evolutionists and creationists both must hold their contrary views purely as matters of faith. There are, however, positive indications that mutant forms called by the evolutionists "new additions" to the world are not modern additions by any means.

First, in this connection, is the fact that nearly every mutation, which has been observed to occur in the fruit-fly in Morgan's laboratories has occurred more than once. The mutation called "white-eye" has occurred 25 times; that called "vestigial" (wing) 6 times; that called "eyeless" 2 times; that called "ebony" 10 times; that called "bar-eye" 2 times; that called "pink" (eye) 11 times; that called "vermilion" (eye) 12 times; that called "dachs" (legs) 2 times (12). These are typical examples of the occurrence of all mutations in this species. "The reappearance of the same mutant," says Morgan, "indicates that we are dealing with a specific and orderly process" (12). He also says, "We must remember that the majority of mutants we find are not new, but have probably been rejected many times by natural selection, for some of the same mutants appear over and over again in our cultures. New ones, too, are continually appearing—new in the sense that we have never seen them before. These, too, have no doubt occurred elsewhere" (12). Does not this repeated appearance of exactly the same form in a species indicate that old things are involved rather than that new things are created each time they appear?

Second, in this connection, is the fact that some mutations which have occurred in modern times and are said to be "new" are known to be hundreds of years old. Prof. Lotsy uses as one of his proofs that mutations are not new the case of a variety of petunia with green-rimmed petals which was observed to arise in 1830 in England and arose again in 1914 in his own garden (11). How many times that mutant form arose unnoticed no one knows. One of the most talked-of mutations of so-called new things in animals is the polled or hornless condition in cattle, which is known to be due to a Mendelian factor. This mutation is very often cited as one of the instances of "new" forms arising by mutation. Professor W. M. Goldsmith (8) of Indiana University says, "The present critic (Goldsmith) would prefer not to deceive his readers into believing that new characters are not arising *de novo* from unexplainable sources. This sudden appearance in plants and animals of new characters which breed true is called a MUTA-

---

157 We find this kind of argument all through the evolutionary discussion. Evolution *must* be true, therefore there are "faults" in nature's arrangements of the geological layers, and "falsifications" in the way nature develops embryos, etc. The theory of evolution is a bald assumption, and natural facts must fit the theory or so much the worse for the facts.

TION and is held by many of the most eminent living scientists to be one of the principal factors which is determining the direction of evolution. Numerous examples of mutation may be found by referring to the index of any recent book dealing with the various problems of Evolution, Genetics and Eugenics. Among the classical examples might be cited the hornless 'Herefords' (1889)." Yet the Greek historian Herodotus (425 B. C.), tells us that the cattle of the ancient Scythians were hornless (16). Hence we know the factor for poll or hornlessness was in existence five hundred years before the time of Christ. A fact worth noticing is that the same mutant forms which have appeared in the fruit-flies with which Morgan experimented appeared also in the same species in the experiments of other men in other parts of the world, although the flies these men have used were not procured from Morgan but were gathered independently in their own localities. The evolutionists explain this condition by saying that the original "creations" of the factors for those mutant forms must have occurred far enough back in the past for the factors to become multiplied and scattered abroad in the germ cells of the species everywhere. How old the factors must be for this to be true we can not say. They must be quite old, to say the least. But is it not a peculiar kind of faith which can believe that factors can be as old as that and yet be sure, as all evolutionists claim to be, that God did not create those factors and put them in the species by an act of special creation as the Scriptures declare?

Modern genetical knowledge gives the following picture of the make-up of the germ or "seed" (to use the Biblical expression), of every "kind" which God created. Each species has a set of chromosomes of a number that is constant (except when such temporary things as non-disjunction and polyploidy occur). These sets of chromosomes are the bearers of the genes, which are in some species exceedingly numerous. The fruit-fly *Drosophila Melanogaster,* with a set of four chromosomes, is estimated to have five thousand genes. Man, with a set of twenty-four chromosomes, has perhaps 100,000 genes, each one able to affect in some way the size of the human body, the shape of the skull, the texture of skin, slant of eye, color of hair and so on. The genes were placed in the species by the Creator at creation, together with a definite mechanism or orderly process by which they could at different times reveal their effects. With the information about genes which modern discovery has given, the color of Adam and Eve can be surmised. Judging from what is known of "multiple factors" for color in wheat, corn, flies and other animals, there are also multiple factors for color of skin in man—many factors for red, black, yellow, white, and these factors have become grouped together in the various races. If there are, as is practically certain, multiple factors for color of skin in man, and if Adam and Eve were mulattos—a shade a mixture of black, white, red, and yellow —it is easy for geneticists to see how their color genes could become grouped and selected by climatic influences so as to form the various colors of the races.

To sum the whole matter up we may say that "mutation" is nothing but the revelation of types within species provided for by the Creator in His acts of special creation.

LITERATURE CITED

1. Babcock, E. B., and Clausen, R. E., *Genetics in Relation to Agriculture,* 1927, pages 239, 246, 251.
2. Bailey, L. H., and Gilbert, A. W., *Plant Breeding,* 1917, pages 91, 90.
3. Burbank, L., *His Methods and Discoveries,* 1914, Vol. II, page 97.
4. Castle, W. E., *Genetics and Eugenics,* 1926, pages 265-266.
5. Conklin, E. G., *Heredity and Environment,* 1925, pages 280, 277, 279.
6. Coulter, M. E., *Outline of Genetics,* 1923, page 10.
7. Gates, R. R., *Mutations and Evolution,* 1921, pages 22, 74.
8. Goldsmith, W. W., *Evolution and Christianity,* 1925, page 61.
9. Jennings, H. S., *Creation by Evolution* (Mason), 1928, page 23.
10. Jones, D. F., *Genetics in Plant and Animal Improvement,* 1925, pages 75; 169-170.
11. Lotsy, J. P., *Evolution by Means of Hybridization,* 1916. pages 38, 31, 38, 55.
12. Morgan, T. H., *The Genetics of Drosophila,* 1925, pages 217-239; 28-32; 23-24. *Evolution and Genetics,* 1925, pages 111-113; *Theory of the Gene,* 1926, pages 66, 91, 66; *Yale Review,* April, 1928.
13. Newmann, H. H., *Readings in Evolution, Genetics, and Eugenics,* 1921, page 364.
14. Sinnott, E. W., and Dunn, L. C., *Principles of Genetics,* 1925, pages 32, 303, 95, 23, 104, 32.
15. Walker H. E., *Genetics,* 1922, page 186.
16. Herodotus, Book IV—29 (Translation by Henry Cary, 1899).

Appendix III

Section 1
HUMAN APPENDIX NOT VESTIGIAL*

The foregoing paragraphs on vestigial organs in man were written 36 years ago, in 1931. Lately (1967) the paragraphs were read by Dr. Robert G. Taylor, an Internal Medicine Specialist. Because the paragraphs contained a few inaccuracies in the light of advances made in the knowledge of the human body, and because evolutionists are prone to repeat the old falsehood that the human appendix is vestigial, the author quotes Dr. Taylor:

"The once loudly proclaimed useless part, the thyroid gland, is now known to be vitally important in the normal body growth, and over-supply or under-supply of this gland's hormone, thyroxine, will result in overactivity or underactivity of all body organs (e.g., rapid heart or slow heart, diarrhea or constipation). Deficiency of this organ at birth causes that hideous deformity called cretinism. The thyroid utilizes the iodine that comes into the system in the food that is eaten. Yet this important part, because its function was unknown, was sixty years ago considered an infallible 'proof' of evolution. Another 'vestigial' part, whose lack of function has been discovered, is the pituitary gland. On the functioning of this gland depends the proper growth of the skeleton and the proper functioning of the thyroid, adrenal, and sex glands. Overactivity of the gland may cause abnormal growth. The giants we see in circuses are victims of overactivity of one of the pituitary's functions. Eliminate material on the pineal gland since the function still remains a mystery. It is known that tumors of the pineal gland will cause abnormal sexual function. It does not have the early childhood anti-sex function which your reference states.

"The function of the thymus and the human appendix are beginning to be understood in the 1960s. Possibly working with these two organs in similar function are lymphoid tissues in the upper human throat which we know as toncils. These three tissues are all a type of lymphoid or lymphatic tissue. Lymphatic tissue wherever it is found has

196

been recognized for years as a 'chain of fortresses protecting the body against invasion of pathogenic organisms.' In other words, the tonsils and the appendix help to prevent disease germs from entering the system.

"As mentioned above, the function of the thymus and appendix is recently coming to light. Their primary function seems to be operating only in the first few months of life, and then, since the work is completed, both of these organs shrivel or atrophy and would seem to the prejudiced evolutionary eye to be vestigial and non-functioning. This activity in the early months of life begins while the human is still in the mother's womb. It concerns the development of immunity and the ability to become immune in later life. We all had measles, but because of these organs our body was able to make antibodies stay with us so that the next time measles attack us nothing obvious happens. The evidence is very suggestive that without the thymus and appendix operation we would continue having attacks of measles (or mumps or chickenpox) every time we were exposed. To date the experimental proof of this is in animals, especially rabbits, but Dr. Robert A. Good of the University of Minnesota believes all his experimental evidence fits the idea that humans are fitted with the same mechanism. The same evidence is suggesting that the so-called thymic death in infants of forty or fifty years ago can now be explained. The infants were not choked by a large thymus gland. Their gland was normal size and had not functioned properly in forming antibodies and had not yet shriveled to the minute size of the thymus of later life. These infants died of an overwhelming viral infection which the thymus (and perhaps the appendix) if it had functioned properly would have combatted with previously made antibodies. *So you see these organs can hardly be called 'vestigial'.*"

---

*Interested persons may consult the article 'Role of the Appendix in Development of Immunologic Capacity' by Sutherland, Archer and Good in PROCEEDINGS OF THE SOCIETY FOR EXPERIMENTAL BIOLOGY AND MEDICINE, University of Minnesota, March 1964 V. 115 P.673 ff. Or, more easily, consult the article, "THE 'USELESS' GLAND THAT GUARDS OUR HEALTH" in the READERS DIGEST, November 1966, p 229 ff.

Section 2

Since Mendel's time much has been learned about heredity about which Mendel could not have dreamed. The gene has been explored. It has been found to be an atom consisting of DNA (deoxyribonucleic acid). It is the only atom which can reproduce itself. So impressed were many people with the discovery of DNA that they believed that the theory of evolution was now proved. DNA however has nothing to do with the truth or falsehood of that theory. Bringing DNA into the discussion of evolution is like a man who is explaining the game of croquet discussing what croquet balls are made of — wood, rubber or plastic, etc.

Index

202